Alive and Ki...

C000276859

Alive and Kicking

Towards a Practical Theology of
Illness and Healing

STEPHEN PATTISON

SCM PRESS LTD

© Stephen Pattison 1989

All rights reserved. No part of this publication may be
reproduced, stored, in a retrieval system, or transmitted,
in any form or by any means, electronic, mechanical,
photocopying, recording or otherwise, without the prior
permission of the publisher, SCM Press Ltd.

British Library Cataloguing in Publication Data
Pattison, Stephen
  Alive and kicking: towards a practical
  theology of illness and healing.
  1. Christianity.
  I. Title
  615.8'52

  ISBN 0-334-01871-4

First published 1989
by SCM Press Ltd
26–30 Tottenham Road, London N1 4BZ

Photoset by Input Typesetting Ltd, London
and printed in Great Britain by
Billing & Sons Ltd, Worcester

Contents

Preface

I had planned to take five years over writing this book. Instead of which, it has actually been written in three months. If I had been able to stick to my original plan, this would have been a large, thorough and systematic review of perspectives on illness drawn from many sources, and of religious responses, actual and possible, to these perspectives. It would have gone some way to establishing the ground for a practical theology of illness and healing for our time.

So much for the ideal book of my dreams! The actual book which is now before you has been occasioned by my leaving my lecturing job at Birmingham University to go and work in the Health Service. I resigned as an academic one day, and the next I decided that I really must try to chart some of the avenues I had explored and publish the results in the hope that they might stimulate others with the necessary time and energy to write the book I wanted to write in the first place. So here you have a series of essays designed to stimulate further enquiry, not my last word on the subject. I hope some of the comments, directions and sources which I include here will be worth stealing and developing.

I have spent some years in researching around the topics of healing and illness as well as being practically involved as a chaplain in various types of institution. This means that my debts to others are enormous. At a formal level I would like to thank my colleagues in the Department of Theology at Birmingham who have provided me with a very congenial environment in which to do research and teaching over the last five years. I must thank the head of Department, Professor Frances Young, who not only leads by example in writing far more than anyone else in the Department, but also allowed me to stay on in my old job over the summer of 1988 to complete this book. My new employers, Central Birmingham Community Health Council, tolerated a long interregnum between appointing me and my actually starting work with them. I acknowledge their patience gratefully. The British Academy made me a small personal research grant for study of the relationship between religion and medicine in socio-historical perspective. I am glad to be able to thank them for their support. Selwyn College, Cambridge, invited me to spend a week there at the expense of their Marsh Fund and this afforded me a very welcome change of scene in the middle of writing the book. I thank them for their generosity. The editor of *Contact* has kindly permitted me to reproduce here material originally presented in that periodical. The encouragement which SCM Press gave me from the beginning was a substantial incentive to finishing the book.

At an individual level a number of people deserve particular mention. The Archbishop of Canterbury is sometimes rather unjustly berated for taking other peoples' ideas and retailing them as his own in his speeches. Had members of his staff not consulted me in relation to one of those speeches, this book would not have been written. The initial stimulus for it was an enquiry from Lambeth which made me realize that I actually had more thoughts on this subject than I had previously supposed. Hugh Macleod, a social historian of religion in my Department, has been a valuable source of reading material and conversational stimulus. Charmian Beer provided friendship, interest and support throughout, as well as reading the manuscript and unfolding to me the further mysteries of the word-processor. Sue Orr and James Woodward stimulated thought and the latter kindly compiled the index.

Ultimately, two people deserve any credit which attaches to the content of this work, Peter Bellamy and Janet Mayer. Not only did they encourage me to write it in the short period of time available, they also gave much of their own time during the period of composition to read and comment on chapters. Without their active, positive interest and encouragement over the months I could not have carried on writing. This book is a celebration of the friendship which Peter and Janet have given me and it is dedicated to them with my love and thanks.

My concluding words must be in defence of the study of theology in universities. The books, papers, and thesis which I have had the opportunity to write have been possible simply because I have had access to university facilities paid for by public money. This public money is fast drying up. Arts subjects in general, and theology in particular, are disappearing from universities. When it is realized that there are less than three hundred theologians working in universities and that this number is diminishing, perhaps there is a case for churches and other outside bodies taking an active financial interest in the future of university theology to ensure continuing research and teaching as well as width and ecumenicity of theological perspective. At the moment, theology appears too religious to secular universities in a pluralist society and not committed enough for Christians in local churches. Unless there is increased interest in theology from outside bodies, its future in higher education is bleak. I cannot research and write books if I do not have a place and time in which to do these things. Even if my research is felt to be vulgar or ephemeral, readers can probably think of university-based thinkers who have helped them develop their own ideas by their writing and teaching. So my plea is that if people find books like this valuable, they stop knocking the theological 'establishment' and start thinking of how they can help to preserve one particular kind of theological enquiry into the next century. I am all for praxis, contextual theology and doing the kind of theology to which everyone can contribute – that is partly why I want to leave the academic world, for a while at least. At the same time, I have to bear witness to the opportunities which academic theology has given me. I would like other people to be able to have access to them in the future.

Birmingham   S.P.
September 1988

Introduction

I want to start as I mean to go on, on a controversial note. Most of the books which I have ever read on religious responses to healing and illness are ephemeral, banal, repetitive, derivative or boring. There is no area of human and religious life which is more important than that of illness and healing, yet very few of the works which spew from the presses of publishers riding the crest of a wave of popular contemporary interest do any kind of justice to the depth and complexity of the subject matter with which they have to deal. With one notable exception, the spirit of hard-headed critical exploration seems to have deserted recent Christian writing on healing and illness.[1] It has been replaced by endless exhortations to become involved in a religious healing ministry, by testimonies from those who have experienced the power of religious healing, and by handy manuals which instruct on how to conduct religious healing.

So, paradoxically, we find ourselves in a situation where there is enormous interest and concern about illness and practical healing ministry amongst Christians (perhaps unparalleled since the earliest days of the church) but this is not in any way matched by appropriate theological assessment and critical evaluation. As for 'secular' provision of healing services and perspectives on illness, for all the attention that they are given by religious writers and thinkers, these might just as well not exist. The National Health Service is a costly, complex, public healing service which touches the lives of thousands of our fellow citizens each day, but its existence and methods find almost no place at all in Christian reflection on healing and illness. Praying for all doctors and nurses in Sunday services is really not enough.

The main aim of this book is to invite Christians concerned about healing and illness in any way at all to think again, and to think both more deeply and more widely about illness and healing amidst the complexities and ambiguities of modern technological society. There is an enormous range of knowledge about these subjects from many different sources; it is sad that so little of it is allowed to penetrate the religious world and to inform Christian healing responses. Clearly, in a short book like this it will not be possible to do more than produce a rough map of some of the terrain which needs to be covered and to explore one or two avenues more thoroughly. My hope is that some of my perceptions and insights may inspire or infuriate others, whether healing practitioners or theologians, so that a more informed and sophisticated debate about healing and illness than has recently been evident can ensue.

In the pages which follow, as I have said, I shall make controversial judgments and assertions. I want to state at the outset, however, that I do not wish to be gratuitously offensive, pejorative or reductionist about others' practices and ideas. If readers feel that their own perceptions are being parodied or misunderstood they should probably ascribe this to my ignorance or incomprehension. I hope they will forgive my errors and misunderstandings and accept my explanation when I say that my reasons for adopting a direct, even polemical tone in places, are largely to energize response and debate with a view to clarifying concepts and ambiguities and engaging at a deeper level. I have no desire to 'knock' people's willingness to help and heal the afflicted. I simply want to encourage them to think more carefully about their assumptions, contexts and methods. Wherever and however people are actually healed, I rejoice. This does not, however, commit me or anyone else to having to believe that all perspectives and practices are equally valid or unproblematic. In fact, I believe that most ways of looking at illness and healing with their accompanying practices have strengths and weaknesses. My assumption is that evaluating these is useful, valuable and necessary if Christians are not to remain unhelpfully naive in their responses. We live in a complicated and sophisticated society; simple or mono-dimensional responses to complex and multi-dimensional phenomena such as healing and illness may betoken a lack of faith in a God who somehow continues to create and to reveal himself in the chaos of contemporary existence. Adequate healing responses, whether 'secular' or more overtly 'religious', must be two-eyed, not monocular or myopic.[2]

My own vision of adequate Christian responses to healing and illness would require that they be situated within incisive, comprehensive and critical awareness. This is an impossible ideal - a fact to which this book bears all too clear witness. I am very aware of its limitations. In the first place, it does not give a comprehensive overview of all the possible ways of looking at illness and healing. Limitations of space and knowledge have led to my having to be selective in the viewpoints I consider. By the same token, secondly, although I have read what I believe to be a representative selection of books on Christian healing, I have made no attempt to read all of those which are available, nor to give a *résumé* of their contents here. I have seen the purpose of this book as being to provide ideas and opinions rather than to be a survey of all relevant material.

Related to this point, thirdly, the book clearly betrays my own prejudices and preferences in looking at this general area. For example, social, sociological and political perspectives on illness and healing are emphasized, while individualistic perspectives are given less weight. This necessary selection can be justified by the fact that the former are far less well understood and used than the latter. But the fact remains that, ideally, both should be given equal space.

Fourthly, over-generalization and lack of specificity in terms of Christian response to healing and illness are often criticized in the text, but at the same time the book is full of over-generalizations. In one chapter, for instance, I deal with mental illness at some length, but in fact there is no such thing as mental illness in general; there are only mental illnesses in particular. Many of the sources upon which I have drawn, in the history of medicine, for example, are painstaking in their methods and modest in their claims. I have press-ganged them into use in the full knowledge that I do not do them or their authors justice. This is a fifth limitation to the present work.

A further, sixth, criticism might be that I raise questions and problems without supplying adequate solutions and answers. It is very easy to criticize things from the Olympian heights of academe, much more difficult and much more important to propose positive, practical alternatives. Finally, there is no conclusion to what is inevitably a partial and fragmentary work. This can only be justified

on the basis that the book is an invitation and a prologue which
only just begins to explore some of the very important issues which
surround illness and healing. The place where the conclusion
should be is, hopefully, the place where the reader will start to
make her own response to the issues I have raised.

Having discussed some of the book's limitations, it is, however,
important to outline just what is in the pages which follow. The
first chapter is a very wide-ranging schematic attempt to set out
some of the key issues which need to be addressed by theologians
and those concerned with the practice of all kinds of healing today.
It indicates areas of research, dialogue, and reflection which require
urgent exploration if Christians are to engage in comprehensive
and well-informed healing responses in the modern world. The
chapter is condensed, terse and programmatic. It is not really
necessary to read it in order to understand the remaining chapters
in the book. Some readers may, therefore, prefer to skip over it,
to omit it altogether, or to return to it after reading the remainder
of the book.

The rest of the book addresses in a preliminary way a few of the
issues raised in the first chapter. The first of these is the fact that
there are many different kinds of disease and illness which are
perceived, experienced and dealt with in very different ways.
Christians tend to talk about illness as if it is essentially one thing
and, by implication, healing responses are also fairly monolithic.
Chapter 2 is intended to show just how many different possible
ways there are of looking at illness and thereby poses the question,
'What is a good and correct healing response?' Every theoretical
perspective has its own practical implications. The challenge to
Christians, and indeed to everyone who is concerned about healing,
is to evaluate different perspectives in order to arrive at specific
healing responses which are appropriate to particular disorders
and situations. The next chapter, chapter 3, evaluates a variety of
specifically Christian responses to illness and healing at the present
time and tries to locate Christian healing within the wider social
order and to draw out the implications of these responses. It
concludes by emphasizing the importance of the socio-political
and conflictual elements in illness and healing which have mostly
been ignored by members of Western churches. These are directly
explored in chapter 4, which suggests that conflict and socio-
political issues are often implicit in many situations of illness and

healing and so they need to be addressed directly by Christians interested in formulating adequate and specific healing responses. These elements are also alluded to in the last two chapters, which consider specifically two very different types of illness. Chapter 5 enquires into mental disorder to discern an appropriate Christian healing response for today, while the last chapter looks at the latest epidemic to hit Western society, AIDS, and considers some of the ways in which Christians have and should respond to its implications. An Appendix on the contemporary relationship between Christians and the medical profession amplifies material relevant to some of the chapters of the main text.

Three final observations. First, in the text I often allude to sources in the social history of medicine and healing. This is partly because I find such history fascinating in its own right and would like to interest others in it, but it is also included because it is relevant. In his book, *The Use and Abuse of the Bible*, Dennis Nineham talks of reading the Bible as being like taking a holiday in a foreign country.[3] Seeing things done differently and observing different social customs, he suggests, broadens our minds and opens them up to a wider range of possible ways of thinking and acting. A journey through social history or social anthropology can have a similar effect; having some kind of historical background to, say, mental illness, relativizes our contemporary, taken-for-granted ways of thinking about it and may help us to take a broader view. It is this kind of thinking which has led me to indulge my interest in the history of medicine here.[4]

Secondly, I should point out that there is no detailed discussion or definition of the meanings of key terms like 'healing' or 'health' in the text. This does not imply that I do not think such discussion is important. Other works, however, contain very adequate discussions of these concepts and readers are referred to the books cited in the appended note if they wish to explore them further.[5]

Lastly, I want to emphasize again the fact that this book is only a starting point for exploration in a very broad, fascinating and important field. Despite recent technological advances and the vast expansion of human knowledge, healing and illness remain mysterious, if fundamental, phenomena. As I hope readers will see for themselves, there is a vast terrain here awaiting the best efforts of mind from theologians and practitioners alike. If this book can kindle some renewed enthusiasm and seriousness of purpose for practical and theoretical voyages of discovery and dialogue, I shall be more than satisfied. So that others can follow in my footsteps and correct my mistakes of fact and interpretation I have included full notes and references. In this way, perhaps, the book can provide some sustaining substance for the journey, not merely signposts for its beginning.

Chapter One

Towards a Fundamental Practical Theology of Healing and Illness: Setting an Agenda

Illness and healing are central to human existence. If you have your health you can do anything; if you are ill, you may be able to do nothing. Healing and illness are also central concerns of religion. It is when people are ill that their faith is experientially verified or refuted. A theology which cannot speak to the issues raised by disease and suffering could well seem a theology not worth having. Observations like these might lead one to expect that contemporary Christianity would be very preoccupied with this area. There is certainly an explosion of interest in religious healing methods, and there is a veritable epidemic of books being published which come mainly from the pens of evangelical and charismatic writers. These seek to encourage the faithful and convert the credulous to the reality of healing revival. But there is an almost complete moratorium on the subject in the world of liberal critical academic theology. If one was to rely on books written by liberal theologians, one might be tempted to believe that illness and healing did not exist.

This book attempts to break a silence which has lasted almost without significant interruption since the publication of Michael Wilson's *The Church is Healing* in 1967.[1] In many ways, that excellent little book marked the high water mark of liberal reflection on healing and illness. Subsequent works like those of Morris Maddocks have drawn extensively on the work of authors like

Lambourne and Wilson and provide excellent summaries of the
thinking of those writers, but in themselves they add little to
fundamental thinking about this area.[2] While much can still be
learned from the work of these fine thinkers, the time has come
for a basic reassessment of illness and healing. The world in which
we live has changed a great deal in two decades. Our knowledge
of disease and health has changed with it. The whole way in which
illness is perceived can now be differently constellated. Christian
theologians and healing practitioners must move forward, rather
than leaning on the received truths of the past whose value must
now be questioned and put into perspective.

A relatively short work such as this cannot itself provide a
fundamental practical theology of healing and illness.[3] What is
written here is only preface to a much wider task, which must
engage the attention of many thinkers and practitioners. My aim
is to raise issues which may stimulate others to react and engage in
their own reflection. Most of this book will be given over to a
selective treatment of a few issues which I believe to be of crucial
interest and importance. In this first chapter, however, I want to
cast a very wide net. I will outline a broad agenda for consideration
by all those who are concerned to relate Christianity to healing and
illness in the last few years of the twentieth century.

The list of issues and areas suggested here is by no means
exhaustive. Some may feel that there are some surprising omissions.
For example, I do not give the philosophy and mechanics of healing
miracles a prominent place because this topic has been worked
over as adequately as it can be already.[4] My hope is to raise topics
which I believe to be important, but neglected. I acknowledge that
a debate over the items for inclusion on an agenda for developing
a critical practical theology of illness and healing would be fruitful
in itself, and I accept that there will be disagreement as to the scope
and nature of my inclusions. Many of the 'agenda items' which I
put forward here are dealt with briefly, almost cryptically in some
cases. Readers should note the extensive notes which accompany
my main points and which sometimes expand them or give directions for further exploration. They should also remember that my
purpose here is to raise a wide range of topics, not to begin to deal
with them in any depth. Here, then, are some of the issues and
questions which require exploration by those concerned to reassess
the relationship between healing, illness and Christianity today.

1. Fragmentation, pluralism and isolation   The whole field of healing and illness is riven by deep and fundamental divisions at practical, theoretical and theological levels. No one can fail to be impressed by the amount of energy, concern and commitment which all kinds of healers from medical consultants to faith healers put into their work. At the same time, it is abundantly clear that nothing is more calculated to bring about controversy and division than proposing different methods and ideas about healing and illness. Church groups are often fundamentally split over the issue of spiritual versus 'orthodox' methods, and healing sometimes becomes a basic test of religious conformity. How is it that an activity which claims to bring wholeness to a broken world and to reunite the church often seems to contribute to brokenness and disunity?

Schisms are not confined to the religious world, of course; there are basic disagreements within medicine as to how disease should be conceived and treated. Recent controversy over 'alternative' or 'complementary' healing methods in medicine are a potent reminder of this, as are arguments amongst gynaecologists, midwives and potential mothers about the nature of pregnancy and birth.[5]

Schism often leads to relative or absolute isolation. One of the fascinating things about healing is the way in which it seems to encourage the emergence of people with a strong sense of individual mission who become cut off from the mainstream of church life, medicine or theology. At a very basic level, it often seems that people divide over whether they are interested in healing or not. If they are interested in it, they tend to be very, sometimes over-enthusiastic; if not, they tend to be utterly indifferent. This has contributed to the ministry of healing being seen as separated from the whole ministry of the church. While enthusiasm and commitment are commendable and inspiring, it is important to explore why this isolation comes about. What exactly is the relationship between institutional healing practices and ideologies and isolated healers or healing communities?

The kinds of fragmentation, pluralism and isolation identified here probably owe something to the centrality and importance of healing and illness in human life. Those who believe they have the power to heal have power indeed, as well as a sense of mission towards the world. This is as true of secular medical practitioners as it is of herbalists or spiritual healers. The possession of expert, life-saving knowledge is a powerful incentive to intolerance and misunderstanding towards those perceived to be in competiton or opposition. When it is married with strong religious convictions as well, the mixture may be explosive.

Fragmentation, pluralism and isolation are keynotes in thinking about healing and illness at all levels. Many of the points which follow reflect this basic perception. If I have over-emphasized it here, it is only to counterbalance any tendency which there may be to discuss this area as if divisions and conflicts did not exist. This is a pervasive temptation for Christians expounding the merits of one particular way of healing. Frequently, they will make it sound as if no other ways are possible, or as if there are no basic conflicts with their co-religionists or health professionals. Often, nothing could be further from the truth.

2. Who heals whom, when, where and why?   There is a great need for basic mapping of terrain. The words 'healing', 'illness' and 'healer' trip easily from our lips. But we do not really have an informed perspective on who the healers are in our society, who they heal, how they carry out their work, or on the ideological underpinnings which support their healing. The work of healers within formal health institutions such as the National Health Service has been reasonably well surveyed. Rigorously collected evidence about other healing methods is much less well developed. When it comes to religious and 'alternative' healing, one has to rely for the most part on the writings either of healers themselves or of the occasional interested observer.[6] Ideally, a full-scale social and historical survey is needed, particularly into recent developments in religious groups, as a preliminary to comparison and theological response. Only by obtaining accurate, comparable, and comprehensive information about contemporary healers, their practices and beliefs, will it really be possible to move towards an adequate practical theology for healing and illness today. It is necessary to know what one is talking about in terms of scale, diversity and spread before one can talk about it intelligently.

3. Illness and illnesses   The existence of different kinds of healer points to the need to consider pluralism in perspectives on disease. Christians, in common with most of the population, tend to talk of illness as if it were a single monolithic entity. Perspectives furnished by sociology, psychology, epidemiology and philosophy, as well as those furnished by the everyday experience of individual sufferers from various disorders, question this kind of monistic outlook. The experience of being ill with chronic depression is very different from that of experiencing acute liver failure or a broken leg; in many ways, the only thing which unites these diverse experiences is the term 'illness'. If it is more appropriate to talk of perspectives on illness in the plural and indeed to talk of illnesses rather than the singular illness, perhaps there is a need to radically re-think Christian responses and theologies so that they reflect more accurately the pluralistic nature of disease itself. This is a point which will be developed further in the next chapter.

4. Explanations of illness   Practical and theoretical explanations of the causes, mechanisms and outcomes of illness abound. Some of these are scientific and explicit, many more are informal and implicit. The idea that one can catch a chill from getting one's feet wet is a familiar example of the latter.[7] Clearly, there is much scope for people to adopt explanations at different levels and, in practice, it seems perfectly possible for many different and even logically contradictory ideas to be held by one individual at the same time. This becomes particularly interesting theologically when matters of primary and secondary causation are raised by people contracting a disease which they conceive to have both a medical and a religious explanation. Perhaps they did something wrong in the past for which they now feel themselves to be being punished by God. The whole area of explanation in illness and how it functions in theory and practice is underdeveloped. Gaining an understanding of what explanations are adopted, by whom, in what circumstances, and to what ends, is a crucial and fascinating area requiring investigation by practical theologians amongst others.[8]

5. Theology, healing and illness   Searching theological investigation has been at a premium amongst those Christians who have become involved in healing and illness on a practical level. The imperative has been to heal, not to understand illness and healing. This is understandable in many ways, but it does seem profoundly unsatisfactory when evangelical thinkers continue to reaffirm what they conceive to be the 'simple' truths of the Bible in relation to this area while liberals ignore theology altogether, or resort to tired clichés and outmoded theological understandings.[9] The significance of disease in human life deserves more attention within the corpus of mainstream academic theology, while practical religious concern badly needs to catch up with recent developments in theology, e.g., in thinking about the nature of God, providence, suffering and evil.[10] The whole of theology could be taught from the issues raised by illness and healing, while these issues badly need the perpsective provided by critical thought about God. There is, then, scope here for a very rewarding, mutually critical and informing dialogue which is long overdue.

6. *Illness, healing and the Bible* The Bible has been a vital imperative and informing force for Christian concern about healing and illness down the ages. Without its influence, especially its rendering of the healing ministry of Jesus, it is doubtful whether Christian concern would have been so vigorous, or so sustained. Yet here again there seems to be a lack of really critical dialogue. Religious practitioners of all theological hues gain inspiration from Jesus' example and command to heal the sick, without appearing to be interested in trying to rediscover what those things might mean in the light of modern biblical scholarship or hermeneutic theory. Each generation must reinterpret the classical Christian tradition for its own time if it is to be faithful in a truthful and relevant way. It is deeply regrettable that such concerns do not seem to have attracted the interest and energy of those concerned about healing today, for modern scholarship has many new insights to offer about the context, person, teaching and ministry of Jesus.[11] The fault does not just lie on one side, though; biblical scholars conduct their researches with little interest in the meaning of illness and healing today.

7. *Values, morality, healing and illness* Values and morality are part of the stuff of religion. They also impinge upon the perception and treatment of the body and disease at all levels. This is clearly apparent in biblical texts where, for example, sin is associated with illness. But there are many, more subtle ways in which values and illness impinge upon each other. Christianity has had an enormous influence on the way in which the body is construed (for example, as the locus for sin), and on mechanisms of social control.[12]

Questions about whether disorder should be regarded as a manifestation of personal evil forces, as a result of personal responsibility for immoral behaviour, or as a result of the randomness of the universe are to some extent questions of values and morality. The clearest examples of this relationship are to be found in Christian reactions to diseases with substantial sexual connotations; consider contemporary attitudes in the churches to AIDS, for instance. It must, however, be recognized that the entire area of the designtion and treatment of illness is riven with moral assumptions and understandings.[13] To every apparently simple physical disorder there is a subtext of morality and value. This has been seen clearly by secular theorists in sociology and philosophy.[14] So far, however, it has mostly eluded contemporary Christian theologians and healing practitioners. Those who have investigated the area at all tend to be more concerned about the ethics of modern health care. For many Christians involved in practical healing concern, even this is not of much interest.

8. Social and political aspects of illness and healing   It cannot be disputed that the ultimate locus of illness is the individual. It should, however, be recognized that social and political factors impinge on the incidence and understanding of illness at all levels. Modern epidemiological studies reveal the extent to which the social distribution of wealth determines what diseases people will contract and sociological studies show the way in which society actually deals with disorder in individuals.[15] Illness cannot simply be seen as a personal and private thing, nor can healing. Different forms of healing are appropriate to varying social contexts, and power relationships affect their emergence, acceptance and success. This is particularly apparent when the rise of the modern medical profession in the Western world is considered; despite the existence of many different kinds of healers and concepts of illness, one very particular viewpoint has come to dominate and prevail for reasons which have as much to do with social power and organization as they do with 'better' knowledge. There is a sociopolitical context for all kinds of healing, even the healing of Jesus. It is important that this should be evaluated and that Christians should not fall into the trap of conceiving illness and healing as pertaining only to individuals. R. A. Lambourne's work is a valuable marker here, but his insights need to be revised, criticized in the light of new perceptions about healing and developed further.[16]

9. *Social organization of healing*   The National Health Service is the biggest single employer in Europe, having over one million staff. It touches the lives of countless people each year, yet in the last ten years almost no attempt has been made, by Christians, to assess and evaluate its strengths and limitations.[17] This is a devastating criticism for those who claim to be concerned about healing in the modern world, especially at a time when the Health Service faces fundamental changes and cuts. How can Christians wishing to promote human flourishing and healing at all levels, ignore the operation of an institution which embodies so directly very particular values and practices aimed at healing the whole population of the country? By comparison with the work of the Health Service, all alternative healing methods and practitioners, including religious ones, pale into insignificance. A new evaluation and practical theology of the organization of health care in this country is long overdue. And, lest it be thought that this is not a central matter for Christian thinkers and practitioners, it should be recalled that any system which embodies values oriented towards the relief of suffering, must be of central concern to an ethical religion. To concentrate on the practices of individual healers while ignoring the work of the social health care system, is to strain off a gnat while swallowing a camel! It must be emphasized that what is required is not necessarily approval of the Health Service, but knowledge and assessment of it so that Christians can both challenge and be challenged by it.

A second and related area which requires critical evaluation, is that of the relationships between different healing groups in society. There has been a tendency within Christian thinking either to despise 'orthodox' medicine and prefer 'alternative', possibly religious, methods (exemplified in its most extreme form by some charismatic groups), or to take exactly the opposite view, praising and desiring co-operation with medicine while remaining deeply suspicious of other practitioners. The time has come to go beyond these entrenched prejudices in the interests of arriving at a more measured assessment of the value of all the different kinds of healing available. Critical evaluation of this sort might enable

Christians to arrive at better informed judgments as to the value of co-operation or distance in regard to the organization of healing.

10. Healing methods Despite the best efforts of many researchers from all disciplines and persuasions, the mechanisms determining whether or not healing takes place remain a mystery.[18] It may be that in the near future light will dawn in this area. In any case, the main task of Christians is not so much to discover how and whether healing 'works', so much as to evaluate the significance, implications and values promoted by various healing methods. So, for example, the debate about whether Jesus did or did not perform miracles and how he did it, is a rather sterile one. The point consists in the significance of Jesus' healings; what did they reveal about the nature of God, of human beings and of disease? Healing methods of any kind require theological evaluation of their significance. Theology also needs the challenge provided by different healing methods with the implicit ideologies and values they promote.

11. Evil, illness and healing The revival in religious healing, which has sometimes been accompanied by renewed interest in the practice of deliverance or exorcism, has heightened awareness of the dynamics of evil in illness. The ministry of deliverance and its implications are amongst the areas which require further investigation from a theological standpoint.[19] But it is not enough for liberal Christians simply to dismiss this area. Evil and wickedness are real phenomena in the lives of most people, and lofty disdain in addressing these issues is not an answer for people who turn to a religion of salvation from all kinds of suffering.[20] There is a deep vein here for theological reflection which may lead not only into a reassessment of religious healing and its theologies of suffering, but may also be fertile in reflecting on other apsects of healing. Is it, for example, illuminating to examine evil within the Health Service, to enquire into the wickedness of doctors, or to talk of secular and religious healers as 'possessed' when they appear to become detached from wider concerns to pursue (sometimes ruthlessly) their own ideas, concerns and methods?[21] While there may be real dangers in using this kind of language, it may be that it is justified in certain circumstances. It will certainly be unfortunate if the contemporary religious healing movement is

allowed to monopolize the language of demonology unchallenged
by perceptions and insights from other quarters, including critical
biblical scholarship.[22]

12. Suffering, illness and healing The perennial problem of
suffering has not been, and cannot be solved by modern theology.
This does not mean, however, that theologians and practitioners
in the area of healing and illness should not continue to wrestle
with it and try to find practical and truthful theodicies.[23] All too
little thought has been given to the use of theodicy in time of
illness. Why do people say things like, 'These things are sent to
try us'? What are they really saying and what implications do such
viewpoints have for their actual response to illness and healing,
and their belief systems and implicit theologies? Here is another
important nexus for practical theology, perhaps *the* important
nexus for it.

13. Particular illnesses I noted above that there was a need to
move away from talking about illness in the singular to talking of
illnesses or perceptions of illness in the plural. The last point in
this agenda is to invite practitioners and theologians concerned
with healing and illness to study particular illnesses and responses
to them, rather than illness and healing in general. It is certainly
true that there are many common denominators between particular
conditions and that often specific responses to them may be very
similar. Generalization is not, therefore, ruled out. Nonetheless,
a lack of specificity and particularity in this regard has not been
helpful either in theory or in practice. Furthermore, generalizations
are likely to be better founded if they rest on detailed knowledge
of discrete disorders. In studying such disorders, many of the
points raised above will doubtless be illuminated and the way will
be cleared for much better practical theologies of illnesses and
healings.

Although the agenda which has been suggested above is by no
means comprehensive, its size and scope are certainly daunting.
Unfortunately, I cannot give thorough consideration to each of the
issues raised in the rest of this book. Some, for example, the socio-
political context of healing and responses to particular diseases, I
can begin to address directly. Others, like mapping the terrain of
healing and the modern history of healing, I must neglect almost

entirely. Nonetheless, I hope that all the points raised form a background to subsequent chapters and that my treatment of them here will provide a broad critical background for the consideration of more specific themes.

Before moving on to address these specific themes, however, I want to highlight a number of key concepts which underlie all the discussions which follow.

The first of these is *ambiguity*. In my research on healing and illness, I have been struck by the ambiguities pervading this area. It is almost as if illness and healing, like beauty, are in the eye of the beholder. There are often ambiguities of interpretation as to whether a condition is good or bad. In the case of mental illness, for example, there has often been extensive debate in religious circles as to whether it represents divine or demonic possession.[24] Similarly, religious people have debated whether illness is a sign of divine disfavour for sins committed or an opportunity provided by a loving father who desires to see spiritual development.[25]

Ambiguity also characterizes healing. Was Jesus an agent of the devil (as the Pharisees may have thought) or did he have God's own authority? Such debates continue into the present in religious circles where much effort is sometimes put into trying to discredit healers who are not of one's own persuasion by suggesting that they do not use divinely approved means or use them in the wrong way. And ambiguity is not confined to religious circles. Medical science has reached heights of technical proficiency unthought of even a century ago, but some of the by-products of this progress seem distinctly ambiguous. What is the point of being able to preserve life using highly expensive technology, if it is not then possible to help people live a life which has some quality? Why cure people if you cannot care for them? Why provide comprehensive medical services, if one of the side effects of doing so is to make people incompetent to look after themselves?[26]

There is probably an element of ambiguity in all ways of perceiving and of healing illness. Every perspective and practice is likely to have strengths and weaknesses, to do good and to do harm. The danger lies in the fact that often healers and sufferers do not share such a perspective on their own beliefs. They think that there is only one way of looking at things and affecting them, and often they are ruthless in their denunciation of those who differ from them. For the practitioner or the sufferer such blind and

dogmatic faith may be justifiable, for often it is the aura of
confidence and certainty which cures.[27] The student of healing and
illness must, however, take a more critical view and be prepared
to look behind the faith system to discover its ambiguities. Perspectives on healing and illness are hotly disputed. This is a tribute to
their importance in people's lives.

A second important element which has struck me in looking at
healing and illness is that of *conflict*. This notion is implicit in the
foregoing discussion of ambiguity but it is also worth highlighting
in its own right. As with religious faith systems, it is the importance
of healing which makes it a battleground for people of different
persuasions. The propensity for religious healing to produce
divisions in churches has already been mentioned, but conflict is
pervasive at all levels and in all kinds of situations where illness
and healing are involved. Demon possession, for example, can in
some situations be interpreted as a muted protest against social
injustice or lack of control and the same interpretation might be
applied to certain modern disorders such as anorexia nervosa or
depression among women. Healing by religious or spiritual means
can, by the same token, be regarded as a form of attempting to
gain power and significance in the world on the part of those who
are dispossessed and unable to exert influence. Some of the spirit-
filled Puritan healers of the seventeenth century, for example,
seem to have used healing as a way of arousing popular political
support and of legitimating their social protest and aspirations;
there is nothing like having God working through you to assure
you that you have a right to influence in the world. The world of
orthodox healing is filled with conflicts between different medical
and para-medical groups and the rise of the medical profession
itself, and its constant attempts to suppress or subordinate alternative forms of healing, forms a text book example of the propensity
towards conflict in the area of healing and illness. It is important
that students of this area should not be seduced by the rhetoric
of healing, wholeness, harmony, unity and peace with which
proponents of particular healing strategies tend to surround themselves. Healing is much too important an issue for everyone to
agree on. There is conflict at every juncture; just because it may
be implicit or disguised does not mean that it is not there. Where
conflict appears to be absent, it is very possible that the voice and
concerns of a minority are being suppressed.[28]

My third underlying key concept is that of *socio-political context*. I have already mentioned this in outlining the agenda for investigation in healing and illness, and indeed I propose to discuss it directly in a later chapter, but I mention it here again because it is something which informs the whole approach of this book. People, perhaps especially Christians engaged in the healing movement, are apt to talk of illness and healing as if they were simply personal phenomena. This represents a very one-sided view, for, as we shall see, the factors which cause or favour the development of disease often lie outside the individual. Furthermore, the whole way that illness is perceived and dealt with in particular societies is heavily dependent on the wider social and political order. Methods of healing do not find acceptance just because they happen to be scientific or effective, they are taken up because they fit in with a wider social and political world view. Thus, the study of social sciences, such as medical sociology, medical anthropology and social psychology, reveals that illness and healing must be seen not in isolation but within a wider social context. The presentation of these phenomena as, for example, pathology of an individual organism, must not be taken simply at face value. Questions must always be asked about the social and political significance of perspectives on healing and illness. For example; Who decides who is ill and who is healthy? Who benefits from the decision-making process and the decisions made? How does this fit in with wider social aspirations? This perspective of 'socio-political suspicion' underlies the whole of the rest of this work and will, I hope, prove an illuminating counter-balance to the apolitical and asocial ways in which healing and illness have tended to be analysed by Christian students of healing in the past.[29]

Finally, I want to underline the importance of the *morality/value dimension* in my treatment of themes in healing and illness. This has been mentioned above and is indeed closely akin to my last point about socio-political context. Morality and values do not simply impinge on medical ethics, although they certainly do that. At a very deep level values inform our actual view of the world, what we see and what we do not and, indeed, cannot see. The fundamental moral grammar of our own world view is so close to us that we find it almost impossible to recognize and examine it; fundamental values and the perceptions which they support appear to us as facts and we cannot distance ourselves from them. Morality in a deep and pervasive sense is to be found in all forms of perception of illness, as well as in all healing theories and methods.[30]

This is one of the main features contributing to contention and conflict in healing; different methods challenge not only other practices, but also fundamental values and world views. Conflicts about basic values should be of great interest to theologians, for Christianity has done much to promote a very distinctive ethics of the body and illness. They are most apparent when sexually associated diseases are examined, but they can be found at all points in the consideration of just about any disease. Even the acquisition of a cold, for example, can be the occasion for a lesson about the responsibility of the individual for her plight which reinforces a very particular world-view and self-concept. Perhaps this point seems somewhat obscure and epigrammatic. If so, I would ask the reader to forbear and simply remain alert to issues of morality and value as they appear in the chapters which follow.

So to the main substance of the book. In the next chapter I begin to outline some very different perspectives of illness and healing from various sources. This is with a view to establishing the opinion which has already been expressed that illness, being a pluriform phenomenon, should be met with a variegated intellectual and practical response from contemporary Christians.

Chapter Two

Perspectives on Illness:
A Kaleidoscope

An important purpose of this book is to examine critically some aspects of illness and Christian responses to it. This, of course, begs the question, What is illness? It is not possible to evaluate responses to a phenomenon when you do not really know to what you are referring. In everyday life, people have no difficulty in using the concept of illness to talk about certain kinds of affliction. To them, this usage seems utterly unproblematic. In fact, this apparently straightforward concept is a nexus for many different understandings and perspectives. The experience of illness is more universal and common than religious experience of God; ways of understanding it are no less complex and pluriform.

The aim of this chapter, then, is to act as a prelude to the rest of the book. It illuminates and shows the complexity of the concept of illness drawing on the resources of modern academic disciplines such as the social sciences and history. While I hope that this will in itself be of interest to readers, it is far from simply being an exercise in abstract curiosity. Different understandings of illness determine different reactions to it. It is impossible to evalute, suggest, or modify religious responses until a map of some of the available perspectives has been constructed. To this end, a number of the more common or significant perspectives on illness will be outlined here, starting with the most common model in our society.[1] This is the biomedical or disease model.

Some of the perspectives outlined here will be very familiar, for example, the psychological perspective which has made the term 'psychosomatic' so much a part of everyday understanding. But ways of looking at illness which may be less familiar or less congenial if no less significant to contemporary Christians are also considered, e.g., perspectives derived from sociology and social anthropology. Inevitably, my account of different viewpoints must be fragmentary and arbitrary. Equally, readers may find themselves more interested in some ways of looking at illness than others. The point is that it is important to realize how diverse perspectives are, and also to recognize the enormously wide and different practical responses which each one implies. Throughout my discussion, I will try to highlight the aspects of cause and effect implied by each model and to draw out its significance for therapeutic action. Towards the end of the chapter, I shall discuss the importance of explanation in illness and consider the use of concepts like 'cause and effect'. A final discussion of implications sets the stage for an evaluation of contemporary Christian responses to illness and healing in the next chapter.

The Medical Model

The most common and dominant conception of illness and its treatment prevalent in our society is the so-called 'medical model'. This model is embodied in our major health-care institutions. It forms the fundamental horizon for medical intervention. Having said this, and acknowledged the pervasiveness and power of this model over the last two centuries, it is actually very difficult to define what its central characteristics really are. It is quite possible that many practising physicians could not easily articulate a definition of it. Engel offers the following rather dense characterization:

> The dominant model of disease today is biomedical, with molecular biology its basic scientific norm. It assumes disease to be fully accounted for by deviations from the norm of measurable biological (somatic) variables. It leaves no room within its framework for the social, psychological, and behavioral dimensions of illness. The biomedical model not only requires that disease be dealt with as an entity independent of social behaviour, it also demands that behavioral aberrations be explained on the basis of disordered somatic (biomedical and

neurophysiological) processes. Thus the biomedical model embraces both reductionism, the philosophic view that complex phenomena are ultimately derived from a single primary principle, and mind-body dualism, the doctrine that separates the mental from the somatic. Here the reductionistic primary principle is physicalistic; that is, it assumes that the language of chemistry and physics will ultimately suffice to explain biological phenomena. From the reductionist viewpoint, the only conceptual tools available to characterize and experimental tools to study biological systems are physical in nature.[2]

The important points to take from this definition for present purposes are these: (1) The medical model concentrates on physical mechanisms; indeed, the body itself is seen somewhat on the lines of a machine. (2) Explanations of pathology are couched in terms of biology, chemistry and physics. (3) Pathology is identified by recognizing undesirable or harmful deviations from biological norms. (4) Pathogens, i.e. things which cause diseases, tend to be regarded almost as independent entities (the most common and clear example of this is that of the invading bacterium or germ). (5) Illness when it occurs is to be seen as occurring within the physiology of the individual sufferer. (6) Treatments and remedies will consist of intervening in the individual's physiology. (7) If no treatments are presently available, they will be discovered by research conducted along rigorous scientific lines.

Much of the recent history of health and illness is couched in terms of the advance of biomedicine. The heroes of this approach are scientists like Pasteur and Virchow who discovered more about harmful micro-organisms and the workings of the body.[3] It has provided powerful tools for fighting all kinds of diseases and it is claimed to be of use for disorders ranging from cancer to mental illness. At an everyday level, people consulting doctors are constantly aware of its influence, for example, when they are offered a prescription for a drug or invited to submit specimens for a laboratory test. It has even provided doctors with their distinctive dress, the laboratory coat!

Many of the criticisms and negative implications of the medical model in theory and practice will be made indirectly below by the consideration of other models and perspectives. Some, however, can usefully be summarized here:

(*a*) The medical model tends to be individualistic in its perceptions and treatments.

(*b*) Because the focus of the medical model is on actual physical pathology, this leads to a curative rather than a preventative stance and, in practice, scientific knowledge about cure may displace an interest in human care.

(*c*) The medical model tends to isolate disease from wider social factors.

(*d*) It has a tendency towards being very aggressive in practice (so patients sometimes feel that they are but a battle ground upon which doctors wage a war against disease).

(*e*) Not all disorders are best seen within the paradigm of the medical model. Chronic disability, for example, would seem to demand a different approach, for many of the problems which have to be coped with are not actually medical ones.

(*f*) Many critics would also question the application of the medical model to mental disorder, given the relative lack of success in finding physical causes and effective medical treatments for it.

(*g*) There are also fundamental problems with the concept of disease. Philosophers have criticized the medical model for talking of disorders as if they have an external and objective existence while this actually seems very problematic.[4]

(*h*) On a practical level, there often seems a good deal of dispute as to how the medical model should operate and the causes and treatments of disease are hotly disputed by doctors themselves. A recent example of this is the argument as to whether cancer is caused by invading viruses or by a misfunction within the human body.

The fact is that, although the medical model looks simple and coherent, it has many problematic aspects and areas of dispute which complicate its theoretical and practical application. While taking note of this, however, it must be remembered that the medical model is just a model, a device used because it has practical usefulness. Its real usefulness has been proven, at least to some extent, in the elimination and relief of illness. Even in moral terms, it can be seen to have considerable advantages because in asserting the objective physical basis for disease it actually removes blame for her condition from the sufferer. This is far from being the case with many other perspectives on illness.[5]

Psychological Perspectives on Illness

There are probably very few people in our society who would want completely to deny any physical or organic basis for illness. Many, however, would say that physical explanations and perspectives on disease are only very partial. There are many other factors which should also be taken into account. Probably the most popular set of alternative or complementary explanations for illness offered in our society comes from the perspective of psychology. In everyday life, people constantly allude to illness being psychosomatic. By this they mean that people's mental perceptions and reactions deeply affect the sort of illnesses they get, the way in which they deal with them, and the possible outcome which may result from them. Used as a pejorative term, the designation 'psychosomatic' can denote the suspicion that an illness in not a real illness at all, but merely a convenient mental fiction adopted by a person to attain particular ends.[6]

There is no shortage of evidence to show how psychological factors such as perception, emotion, life events and character impinge upon illness. Although the precise 'mechanisms' of psychological and physical interaction are often obscure, *prima facie* one would expect this kind of relationship to exist. All of human life is based on physiology. Emotions, for example, have a physiological basis. Thus, it is easy to observe an angry person turning red, a frightened person turning white as their body tissues lose blood, or to understand why anxiety appears to inflame the lining of the stomach in such a way as to make ulceration more likely.

Recent research has shown how character-type may affect the likelihood of a person acquiring coronary heart disease; intensely competitive people are more likely to experience it than people with a more relaxed approach to life.[7] The same sort of research has been done with cancer patients. It has demonstrated that people are more prone to this disease if they are the kind of people who need to control life events and do not find it easy to express their emotions.[8] The stress caused by life events as a factor in becoming ill has also been explored. Bereaved people are more vulnerable to disease and death, and even a change in life or circumstances can heighten vulnerability.[9] It seems likely that emotions play a large part in diseases such as hypertension, asthma, ulcerative colitis and peptic ulcers.

Behavioural psychology has contributed much to understanding and trying to prevent illness. The insights of behavioural psychology underlie a great deal of health education theory, for much illness is caused by the practice of bad habits which have been learned, e.g., smoking, eating a poor diet. Behaviourists suggest that to overcome this kind of problem and so improve the health of the population new attitudes and practices must be taught.[10]

Psychological insights into the factors surrounding the incidence of illness complement and broaden those of the medical model. Once again, the focus tends to be on the individual, though this time on her character and behaviour rather than her microbiological constitution. The remedies suggested by psychological techniques range from work with individuals to help them relax, through to behaviourally oriented programmes of social education. To this extent, psychological insights tend toward a prophylactic or preventive viewpoint rather than towards curing diseases when they have actually occurred. There can be no doubt that social education and personal counselling and treatment might have an enormous influence on the incidence and course of illness in our society.

There are aspects of this perspective which may be regarded as very negative. The most serious of these is the fact that it is very easy to blame the individual for her illness. It was because she herself did not change her attitudes or habits that she now finds herself ill with cancer or heart disease. This might be called the proper attribution of responsibility so an individual can take control of her own life. On the other hand, it might be designated victim blaming and it is implicitly but strongly questioned by more societally-oriented approaches to illness which I shall now outline.[11]

Epidemiological and Social Administrative Approaches to Illness

Not all doctors trained using the paradigm of the medical model confine their interest to the study of disorder within the individual. Epidemiologists and their clinical counterparts, community physicians, make their primary focus of interest the distribution of disease in whole populations. Their concern is to understand why diseases occur in particular populations at particular times and what significant factors bear upon these occurrences. Inevitably, this leads them to have to take into account many features which at first sight seem to be nothing directly to do with disease or health care. Thus, one of the heroes of community medicine, Dr Snow, established his reputation by showing that the cholera bacillus was transmitted in water supplies which had become polluted. The prophylactic response to this situation was to ensure clean public water supplies, a move which was only made possible by essentially non-therapeutic and political means.[12]

Snow's successors have gone on to show the continuing importance of social and political factors in the prevention, incidence and cure of illness. They have also criticized undue optimism about the apparent effectiveness of medical interventions. Thomas McKeown, for example, in his famous study, *The Role of Medicine* (1979), argues that medicine has contributed very little to the aggregate growth of public health in the last two centuries. The great epidemics of infectious disease which used to carry off so many citizens have been eliminated more by better hygiene, nutrition, sanitation and living conditions than by new therapeutic methods whose beneficial effects are confined to fairly narrow areas such as surgical advances.[13]

In giving priority to wider social and political factors in the prevention and treatment of disease, epidemiologists find much sympathy amongst analysts of social policy and administration. The DHSS report, *Inequalities in Health* (better known as *The Black Report* after the name of the chairman of the working party which produced it, Sir Douglas Black), provides a comprehensive overview of the relationship of morbidity and mortality to social and economic structure.[14] It clearly shows that the types and severity of disease as well as mortality are closely linked to factors such as race, gender, geographical location and, especially, socio-economic class position:

> There are marked inequalities in health between the social classes in Britain . . . Mortality tends to rise inversely with falling occupational rank or status, for both sexes and at all ages. At birth and in the first month of life twice as many babies of unskilled manual parents as of professional parents die, and in the next eleven months of life nearly three times as many boys

and more than three times as many girls, respectively, die. In the later years of childhood the ratio of deaths in the poorest class falls to between one and a half and two times that of the wealthiest class, but increases again in early adulthood before falling again in middle and old age.[15]

The authors of the report suggested changes in the health and social services costing about two billion pounds to deal with deficiencies in health care provision. They were also quite clear that the battle against inequalities in health has to be situated within a much wider strategy to obtain wider social equality and justice. Not surprisingly, this overtly political formulation of a way of combatting the inequitable distribution of illness did not find favour with the government of the day. A subsequent report which showed the continuing and deepening health divide between the different classes in society published in 1987 received similar short shrift.[16]

While the ultimate locus of pathology may be the suffering individual, there are all sorts of wider factors which bear upon whether such an individual becomes ill or not and what happens to her once she is ill. Illness, therefore, has to be situated within a much wider social and moral horizon. Its prevention and cure have substantial political implications. 'Treatment' within such a perspective becomes a matter of social restructuring and reorganization rather than personal therapeutic intervention or health education to modify individual behaviour. Unlike the perspectives offered by the medical and psychological perspectives on disorder, responsibility and blame for illness are placed with social and political institutions, rather than with or in the sick individual person. Aspects of this perspective are complemented and modified by the perceptions of sociologists about illness which follow.

Sociological Perspectives on Illness

Sociological analysis of illness starts by making a fundamental distinction between *disease* which is taken to be the objective and observable existence of pathological abnormality, *illness* which is taken to be the presence of symptoms of disorder which are perceived subjectively, and *sickness* which is held to be a socially sanctioned role.[17] This distinction is a useful one. It allows us to discriminate between the *objective presence of pathology* which does not necessarily have any overt effect on a person (many people have diseases like cancer without knowing so because it does not affect their sense of well-being), the *subjective perception of symptoms* (some people – for example those manifesting Munchausen's syndrome – have nothing organically wrong with them yet perceive themselves to be very ill because of their many symptoms), and the way in which disease is *socially recognized* and dealt with as sickness (it is possible to be very ill objectively yet to behave in such a way that one is not perceived to be sick; hence some people who may in fact be very near to death through disease may not be recognized as being sick).

Illness behaviour or sickness is regarded as a particular kind of deviance by sociologists.[18] That is to say, it is regarded as socially undesirable. In society, undesirable behaviour is usually discouraged by means of positive and negative sanctions, i.e. rewards and punishments. In the case of criminality, deviance from desirable social norms is thought to emanate from the choice of the criminal. Punishment to induce conformity is therefore the chosen method of sanction. Illness, however, presents a special case. The person who is ill is not deemed responsible for his or her deviant behaviour. This person acquires a very particular deviant role, the sick role.[19] When someone is perceived to be sick, she is relieved of normal social responsibilities such as working. She is not held responsible for her misfortune (a person who is found not really to be ill is often stripped of the sick role and may be punished in informal ways). Her position is regarded as a misfortune from which she is supposed to want to escape (failure to want to get well may also be punished). Finally, she is obliged to seek medical help, doctors being the 'gate keepers' of the sick role who designate whether an illness is real or not.

There are several intriguing corollaries to this basic perspective that sickness is a deviant contravention of social norms. First, what is thought to be sickness varies from society to society, from time to time and from place to place. Sometimes disease can be accepted as normal or even desirable; the Greeks before Hippocrates thought epilepsy to be a sign of divine favour and inspiration, for example. There is also the example of a South American Indian tribe who all have a particular type of skin cancer and so regard members without this disease as deviants.[20] In the contemporary world there has recently been much controversy over whether Soviet dissidents are appropriately labelled as sick, and in Britain members of ethnic minorities are sometimes diagnosed as mentally ill by medical practitioners when members of their own communities would not regard them as sick at all.[21] The identification of sickness is, then, heavily contextual. This is particularly true when obvious serious physical pathology is hard to discern.

The examples cited bring up another very important point, that of social control. From the vantage point of sociologists and other analysts, medicine forms an important part of the apparatus of social control because it works for the elimination of some types of behaviour and the fostering of other, more desirable, kinds.[22] Often this is to the advantage of sufferers who receive expert and appropriate help when they need it to restore them to adequate social functioning. Sometimes, however, it can seem oppressive. People suffering from mental disorder can feel heavily stigmatized by a diagnosis of, say, schizophrenia. The diagnosis itself may prevent them from ever playing a full part in society again. Until very recently, homosexuality was regarded as a disease. This label has proved offensive to many homosexual people who perceive themselves as being normal and well, not as being ill. The attribution of illness removes responsibilities, but it can also remove rights and civil liberties in a quite draconian manner. A person who is chronically ill may find that he is treated as something less than a full adult. Likewise, a person who is found to be criminally insane, 'mad' rather than 'bad', can find himself forcibly and permanently confined and obliged to receive treatment. His criminal counterpart is not coerced in this way and has the prospect of release into society when his judicially imposed sentence is completed. The significance of the attribution of sickness must not be underestimated. Nor must it be uncritically applauded in all circumstances. It creates problems within the role of health care professionals.[23]

The process whereby somebody comes to be recognized as sick in a society is a very complex one. It involves factors such as the visibility of their symptoms, the degree to which symptoms interfere with their fulfilling social expectations, their duration and severity, and access to health care facilities and personnel who might be able to officially designate illness.[24] The official gatekeepers of the sick role have a pre-eminent role in this process. In

our society, these gate-keepers are medically qualified practitioners. For the most part, doctors are perceived to be benevolent
technocrats. Sociological studies of the role of doctors in society
generally and in personal encounters with patients in particular
throw suspicion on the benevolence and open-mindedness of these
practitioners. Freidson, for example, argues that doctors are more
likely to follow the norms of their professional peers than to be
directly responsive to the needs of their patients.[25] In common with
many other researchers, he points out the upper-class background
of doctors and shows the enormous gap in terms of communication,
power and influence which exists between them and their clientele.
Robinson articulates this point thus:

> The professional's views, moulded by clinical experience and
> training, may differ in emphasis, detail or ordering of priorities
> from the patient's views, influenced by the need to cope with a
> particular problem and the range of possible responses to it.[26]

The doctor – patient relationship is asymmetrical in terms of
power and access to resources.[27] This can make the sufferer very
vulnerable. It means that, at least occasionally, patients may find
that their best interests are not served by medical professionals.
The case of misunderstood poorly-educated Afro-Caribbeans being
misdiagnosed as mentally ill and confined against their will, is one
extreme example of this, but many patients have the experience of
being maltreated by socially superior doctors acting more on their
own cultural values than on medical diagnosis and knowledge.
Thus many doctors take it upon themselves to diagnose people
who hurt themselves while drunk, try to commit suicide, or
complain of low back pain as 'malingerers', especially if they come
from lower class or very different cultural backgrounds from
themselves. Such patients were colloquially termed 'the rubbish'
in the casualty department of one hospital in which I worked; this
is hardly a medical diagnostic term!

Sociological perspectives on illness and its treatment sensitize
us to the contextual construction and control of disorder. They
make us aware of the ways in which sickness is very differently
perceived and handled according to different social norms. The
sociological viewpoint does not itself prescribe ways of dealing with
illness. It is predominantly descriptive rather than prescriptive. It
strongly implies that we must be circumspect in attributing the

sick role to individuals in society. We must be careful to recognize the extent to which such ascriptions fit into wider social norms and values. The powerful role of moral evaluation which is allowed to therapists and gate-keepers must be kept under critical review if the recognition of sickness is to remain a benevolent rather than an authoritarian activity. In terms of apportioning blame or responsibility, sociological perspectives suggest that the attribution of sickness is a matter which is negotiated between the individual and wider society. Society, however, has the upper hand in defining and designating what sickness shall be taken to be. Socio-cultural and relativistic perspectives on illness are now further explored in considerations of medical anthropology, social discourse and the history of medicine.

Anthropological Perspectives on Illness

Anthropologists are perhaps usually thought of as people who spend their time studying so-called primitive or pre-literate cultures in remote parts of the Third World. It may, therefore, come as a surprise to some readers to discover that there is a burgeoning interest in applying anthropological methods to our own culture and to studying illness in British society from an anthropological perspective.[28]

Medical anthropologists aim to situate illness and responses to it within a particular culture or sub-culture. A culture is defined as

a set of guidelines (both explicit and implicit) which an individual inherits as a member of a particular society, and which tells him how to *view* the world, and how to *behave* in it in relation to other people, to supernatural forces or gods, and to the natural environment.[29]

Medical anthropology itself is about

how people in different cultures and social groups explain the causes of ill-health, the types of treatment they believe in, and to whom they turn if they do get ill. It is also the study of how these beliefs and practices relate to biological changes in the human organism, in both health and disease.[30]

The perspective offered by medical anthropology highlights many different and interesting things about illness. First, it makes us aware of the fact that there are thousands of different ways of looking at illness, both between different societies and even within the same society. This can be illustrated by comparing traditional African understandings of illness with those of scientific Western biomedicine. Traditional African understandings focus on the cause of illness rather than its symptoms or treatment, they are more concerned with *why* a person has become ill than with the question of *how* a person has become ill. Causation is viewed in terms of divine intervention or human malevolence; compare the 'neutral' scientific understandings of Western biomedicine.[31]

Similar disparities of understanding exist in our own culture. In a study of attitudes towards colds and fevers experienced by patients in a North London general practice, Cecil Helman was able to show that patients operated on a completely different understanding of illness from that offered by scientific medicine. They had a 'folk' view which allowed them to view germs, for example, along the same lines as people in non-literate societies view evil spirits:

> When asked about the attributes of Germs, most patients give the following description. Germs are described as living, invisible malevolent entities. They have no free existence in nature, but exist only in or among people. They are though of as occuring (sic) in a cloud of tiny particles, or as a tiny, invisible, single 'insect'. They traverse the spaces between people by travelling in the air or in the breath. Germs causing gastrointestinal symptoms are seen as more 'insectlike' (Bugs), and are larger in size than those Germs causing other symptoms. Germs have personalities; these are expressed in, and can be recognised by, the various symptoms they cause. . . . The Germ, however, may only reveal its true personality in stages, during the course of the disease.[32]

This extract points up another important insight from medical anthropology, the fact that understandings of cause and effect in illness are radically different between and within different cultures. Some people in some cultures, for example, will adopt exogenous explanations of illness. That is to say, they will see illness as something which attacks them from the outside or perhaps from heaven. Others adopt endogenous explanations which locate the causes of illness inside the body. Genetic and psychotherapeutic explanations are of the latter kind, while environmental and demonic possession explanations are of the former sort.[33]

Implicit in the former point is the vital importance of meaning in illness. In many ways, the crisis of illness represents a crisis of meaning as much as any kind of physical event. Healing consists, at least in part, in finding a sense of meaning to events by various different kinds of explanation, understanding and behaviour. The whole experience of illness is shaped by cultural meanings and understandings even if underlying biological realities, e.g., the broken leg, remain the same. Medical systems should be regarded as particular ways of organizing meanings. Kleinman suggests that health care systems are cultural systems which articulate illness as a cultural idiom which links beliefs about disease causation, the experience of symptoms, specific illness behaviour patterns, treatment alternatives, therapeutic practices and the evaluation of treatment outcomes.[34]

A corollary point is that the whole experience of illness and the way in which it is understood, construed and treated is closely related to cultural meanings and values. This is as true of Western societies as of any others. So, for example, Western biomedicine with its scientific language and its focus on individual pathology fits in with a generally secular view of the universe and a strong emphasis on the supreme importance of the individual as the basic unit of social discourse. Medical understandings, then, are not simply generated by medical institutions and discourse. Even if they were, they would not be sustainable if they did not chime in with the social and cultural setting of which they must form a part.

Different understandings of illness and its treatment can exist alongside each other. They will be changed when society changes. 'Official' explanations may differ from private ones. Health-care systems embodying different values will compete with each other at various levels. For example, in our own society there are official healers who work with the biomedical model of illness, alternative healers who work with, say, a humoral view of illness, and folk healers who work with people in a totally informal way. It is of vital practical importance to recognize this huge cultural pluralism of views and practices because these things have an active effect on the way we respond to disease and illness and affect our capacity to communicate with sufferers and healers. If, for example, a working-class woman, through her experience of having little choice in life, comes to see major misfortunes such as contracting lung cancer as having nothing to do with the fact that she smokes cigarettes because she has no sense of her own agency and power, there is no point in doctors and other proponents of individual autonomy and choice exhorting her to look after herself. The fundamental cultural gap is too great.[35]

The perspectives offered by medical anthropology are radically relativizing. They suggest that we must be very careful to ensure that we really try to understand different people's views of illness and realize that these views may have a coherence and utility to them, even if this may not be apparent at first sight. Just because someone appears to reject biomedical descriptions of illness, it does not mean that their understanding is invalid within their own cultural context. There are many different understandings of illness and its treatment. These have to be seen against a very broad social and cultural setting. Once again, the medical anthropological approach places understanding before blame in dealing with illness. It suggests that whatever the biological realities of illness, the meanings and methods associated with it are a product of dynamic social interaction.

Social Discourse and Metaphors

Both sociological and medical anthropological perspectives on illness have suggested that the whole process of understanding disease and dealing with it is heavily value-laden because it takes place within a particular social context. This perception is amplified by the realization that even the language and conceptualizations used to describe illness are freighted with values. This is because language itself is socially constructed. We cannot know reality independently of our own particular intellectual constructions of it. This means that in many ways we see or experience what we *think* we see and experience; and our thinking is structured by socially-conditioned linguistic rules and metaphors which in themselves embody deep metaphors.[36]

This is the perception of analysts of social discourse such as the French philosopher and historian Michel Foucault. Foucault does not deny the ultimate reality of disease – as an AIDS sufferer, he must have been all too aware of the horrors of its existence. What he suggests, and this is a notion which theologians would assent to in relation to discourse about God, is that our experience of reality and our knowledge about it is refracted by our linguistic understandings, which are at the most fundamental level loaded with values. In a sense, then, language or discourse actually constructs reality as well as describing it.[37] In relation to disease, it could be said that it is our language about it which shapes it and gives it reality.

These rather abstract reflections are given greater substance by David Armstrong, who draws on Foucault's thought to talk of the political anatomy of the body.[38] Armstrong suggests that the way we see bodies today is actually a product of our own conceptualizations. We have evolved a very particular language to talk of the physiology of the body, but there have been other languages in the past which have construed it in totally different ways. These have led to people actually seeing completely different things and acting on bodies in different ways. A vivid example of discourse structuring perception can be given by citing the example of mediaeval anatomists who persisted in portraying the human liver as having five points. Despite the fact that they had direct access to human livers, these anatomists actually drew what they had been led to expect to see by reading anatomical textbooks.[39] A similar example is found in the evolution of anatomical portrayals of the female human skeleton. Until the nineteenth century, in anatomical atlases male and female skeletons were presented as being exactly the same. Anatomists actually saw them as being the same. It was only when sexual differences became important for ideological and cultural reasons that anatomists began to see women's skeletons as being distinctive.[40] If solid organs like bones and livers can be perceived so differently according to cultural context and belief, is it really possible to believe that any representation of reality is definitive and truthful?

Foucault himself describes an eighteenth-century French physician who treated a hysteric by making her take frequent baths and then reported seeing 'membranous tissues like pieces of damp parchment . . . peel away with some slight discomfort, and these were passed daily with the urine.'[41] Armstrong comments:

> In terms of the twentieth-century anatomical atlas which informs the gaze deep into the body such observations are virtually

unintelligible because, at the moment the modern atlas made its appearance, the old languages, the ancient ways of seeing, disappeared.[42]

Armstrong concludes: 'In effect, what the student sees is not the atlas as a representation of the body, but the body as a representation of the atlas.'[43]

This fascinating perspective, which clearly shows how knowledge structures reality as well as how reality structures knowledge, is complemented by theorists who have tried to unearth the deep, value-bearing metaphors with which diseases have been described. Susan Sontag in *Illness as Metaphor* shows the way in which tuberculosis and cancer have become bound up with wider descriptions and assumptions about social reality.[44] For example, in the nineteenth century, tuberculosis was seen as romantic and in some ways very attractive as a disease. On the other hand, in our own century, cancer has become a metaphor for all that is evil and undesirable in the body of society as well as in the individual sufferer. The language and metaphors used to describe other diseases, particularly sexually associated diseases like AIDS, are a rich field for linguistic analysis and investigation.[45]

Discourse analysis and the critical examination of the metaphors underlying the language of disease once again alert us to the dangers of thinking of illness in uncritically concrete terms. Our understandings are always relative and value-laden, and we have no direct access to the essence of disease, only to our various interpretations of it. That is not to say that some descriptions and concepts are not better, more complete, more adequate or more useful than others.

Practical questions which arise from this kind of perspective include those about power and relative influence; for example, *whose* knowledge and language is to be regarded as normative and whose perspectives are to be ignored? These questions relate very closely to issues of causation, responsibility and blame in discerning and treating illness. The social and linguistic construction of AIDS as a sexually transmitted disease, for example, has led to very particular responses to sufferers which are completely different from those which might be expected if the disease were construed in the same terms as, say, measles. The latter construction would suggest that sympathy and care are deserved because it is a misfortune; the former construction has allowed many to react to people with AIDS as the authors of their own destruction who deserve punishment for their supposed misdeeds.[46]

Historical Perspectives on Illness

The final perspective on illness to be considered here is that offered by the history of medical thought. In some ways, this is similar to the vantage point provided by medical anthropology, for it involves the examination of cultures removed from us in time, if not in space. There simply is not room to give a comprehensive outline of the history of the Western medical tradition here, but even a short account of some of the main features in its evolution serves to show how relative and specific the perspective of Western biomedicine really is.[47]

Before the advent of the Hippocratic tradition, illness was seen primarily as punishment by the gods. Hippocrates dispelled the idea that epilepsy was a divinely given illness and insisted on treating disease as a natural phenomenon as did his successors in the humanistic Greek tradition. The main conceptual framework for understanding and treating illness became that of humoral medicine. This tradition survived until the seventeenth century and shaped Western medicine. It must be noted, however, that it did not entirely supplant other understandings and traditions. Divine providence was supposed to rule over all things in the Middle Ages and epidemics were seen as evidence of divine wrath right up till the beginning of the nineteenth century. Keith Thomas's work on religion and the decline of magic in the sixteenth and seventeenth centuries witnesses to the existence of traditional healing using herbs and to the continuation of magical healing using charms.[48] Chemistry and biology only began to inform healing in the seventeenth and eighteenth centuries. Arguably, modern biomedicine, which began to take its present form in the nineteenth century, did not really start to achieve conspicuous acceptance and success until our own time. Contemporary readers will be well aware of the continuing existence of healing theories and practitioners whose frame of reference is now supposed to be completely out of date. Homoeopaths draw on the ancient tradition of treating like with like; holistic healers commend the concept of balanced and good life-style associated for centuries with the

Hippocratic tradition of regimen; astrologers continue to minister to the needs of the troubled and ill while various kinds of religious and spiritual healing flourish anew.

The perspective offered by the history of medicine suggests that we must be wary of absolutizing one very particular way of understanding illness, no matter how dominant, fixed or successful it may seem to be at the present time. Western biomedicine is only one very recent newcomer to thinking about illness. In practical terms, many would dispute its benevolence, comprehensiveness, assumptions and efficiency.[49] Clearly the assumptions upon which biomedicine works and the techniques which it uses are culturally necessitated and conditioned. This partly explains its conspicuous lack of success in developing countries which lack the facilities of high technology because of a lack of capital to pay for them. There is no reason to suppose that in due course it might not be supplanted by some other healing system. The physicians working in the Hippocratic tradition assumed that their system was the correct one and that nothing different could be devised. History has shown them to be wrong. Each culture and era has to formulate its own healing systems. None of these can, or should, be absolutized.

These are just a few of the theoretical perspectives which are available for thinking about illness. Obviously, my coverage of very complex and detailed scholarly material here has only been very scanty. Equally obviously, I have left out some important issues and perspectives. I am particularly conscious of omitting discussion of the philosophy of disease and illness. Much serious thought and discussion in philosophy has been devoted to the nature of diseases, their common characteristics, their classification and their inner nature.[50] These matters are far from unimportant but do demand considerable abstraction and detailed argument which seems redundant here for present purposes. Soon I shall try to draw out the significance of putting all the perspectives on illness outlined above together in this way. First, however, some space must be devoted to discussing the notion of cause and effect in illness and to the nature and use of explanation in coping with disease.

Cause and Effect in Illness

People who have been extensively influenced by the culture of Western biomedicine (including myself and, presumably, most readers) tend to see illness primarily in terms of identifiable cause and effect. If something goes wrong with a body, the thing to do is to identify a clear cause (social or physical) and then to deal with it. This has been a powerful paradigm for Western science generally and for modern biomedicine in particular. It fits in well with a mechanistic view of the world and with modern predilections for solving problems. My purpose in pointing this out is not to discredit this way of going about things but to bring to consciousness the fact that this is a very particular way of looking at the world and misfortune. It is also an inadequate way of doing so in so far as clear causal connections are often lacking in disease and misfortune. We are constantly exposed to microbes of all sorts, we are told, and yet we are not all constantly ill. Sometimes this may be explicable. Often, however, there is no good reason why we should not be afflicted. This was a problem which beset people in the Middle Ages. Why was it that some people were struck down by plague while other residents of the same house were unaffected? Sometimes they solved this puzzle by attributing the illness to God's desire to punish particular people, but such explanations hardly sufficed, as the innocent seemed to suffer as much as the guilty. The point is that often phenomena are not the straightforward effects of a particular identifiable cause.

When using the language of cause and effect in relation to illness and misfortune the following points should be borne in mind.

1. Often there is no direct correlation between a particular cause and a certain effect.

2. It is useful to recognize that there are intervening variables between a particular cause and a certain effect.

3. By the same token, it is sensible to distinguish primary and secondary causation.

4. It is also useful to take account of constraints on a situation or phenomenon instead of simply talking of cause and effect.[51]

The language of cause and effect is used in everyday life as a way of abstracting from an exceedingly complex reality and of talking simply about it. Its usefulness lies in its being able to set a direction for enquiry and practical effort so that a situation may be understood and perhaps ameliorated. This should not be allowed to obscure the fact that there are really very few straightforward causal relationships in the world, particularly in the complex and value-laden world of illness. Thus it is true that lower-class people in Britain suffer from more and different kinds of illness than their wealthier compatriots. Nonetheless, the reasons and mechanisms why precisely this comes to be the case are obscure. It is this which prevents it from being possible to predict what diseases any particular poor person might get and when exactly he or she might die. The language of cause and effect at its best describes probabilities and possible relationships. It is seldom a comprehensive or totally adequate description of reality. It is necessary to emphasize this here, as there will certainly be moments in the rest of this book where it will be expedient to fall into the assumptions of simple cause and effect for the sake of economy and intelligibility.

Explanation

Explanations are very important in relation to illness. Their purpose is to outline the cause of disease and to prescribe a course of action which will lead to a satisfactory outcome, i.e., to healing. Explanations of illness are very powerful. They prescribe what is good and valuable (identifying a state of being as an illness involves defining it as undesirable and unacceptable); they describe the situations in which sufferers find themselves; and they set out a course of action which will restore them to health. Thus the people who formulate such explanations can be enormously significant and influential, particularly if they occupy a position of high social status within their society, such as medical practitioners do in ours.

Because of the importance of values in explanations of illness which clearly designate what is good/desirable over against what is bad/undesirable, it is possible to describe them as moral explanations in the very broadest sense of the term. It is also possible to construe them as spiritual explanations as they deal with what is of utmost importance to people, invite belief and commitment at a most fundamental level of life, and project forward to future hope. All this is by way of saying that medical explanations are of enormous significance for theologians and for Christians generally. Explanations of illness from different perspectives must be evaluated very carefully and critically, for they both describe and shape the world in which the sufferer lives.

Sufferers, of course, also have their own explanations for being where they are and experiencing what they experience. Often these are set out as stories rather than diagnostic formulae. They constitute 'unofficial' explanations which contrast with the 'official' ones expounded by professional healers.[52] While the explanations of ill people may be less formal than those of professional healers, they are no less important or influential. One of the most fascinating things about perspectives on illness is that we all seem to be capable of adopting several different perspectives on our condition at the same time. So, for example, patients might visit the surgery of their doctor to obtain modern pharmaceutical preparations while believing at another level that their cold is due to their feet getting wet (a notion derived from humoral medicine), or at another that they are receiving some sort of retribution for their pig-headedness and obstinacy in going out in the rain at all. Similarly, patients in hospital at one level seem happy to believe that their cancer is an arbitrarily contracted medical condition; but they can hold this in tandem with the idea that they are responsible for their condition because of their former misdeeds, or because God is punishing them.

The explanations which individuals offer for their plight are frequently multi-dimensional in this way. It is often difficult to discern which perspective on illness is actually operative at any particular moment, or in what way it affects their recovery. One thing, however, seems fairly certain. The explanations which people adopt in themselves make them feel better by helping them to feel in control of their own situation. This is graphically illustrated in a number of research papers by doctors and psychologists which show that people would prefer to see themselves as guilty of causing their own illnesses or those of others rather than seeing them as simply arbitrary occurrences in an unjust world.[53] Here again, then, the need to identify cause and effect arises so that people can feel that they are, at least to some extent, in control of their own destiny in a meaningful world which has clear patterns of order.

The types, range, proponents and situations in which different types of explanation are elicited should be of great interest to theologians and healing practitioners. It is always important to be critically aware of the sort of explanation which is offered in time of illness, who offers it, in what circumstances, and to whom. The function of explanation must also be examined; is it offered as a prelude to action, as a comfort in time of despair or as a contribution to reasoning about a particular situation? All of these functions for explanation are legitimate in their place. If their context and purpose is not understood, however, they may be confusing, misleading or damaging. Explanation in confronting and dealing with illness needs a book in itself. This brief consideration has been offered simply to alert readers to some of the theoretical and practical implications of the explanatory themes and perspectives which will fill the rest of these pages.

Conclusion

My purpose in assembling a large number of different perspectives on illness has been to make more complex the vision of what illness is. The fact is that there is no one correct way of looking at illness. There are many very different and helpful ways of thinking about this phenomenon in the contemporary world.

Some of the perspectives offered above are complementary to one another, at least at some levels. So, for example, there are many points at which the medical model and the psychological perspective reinforce each other. But there are certainly tensions and overt and implicit disagreements between many of the perspectives. Most obviously, the sociological and medical anthropological perspectives implicitly question the hegemony of the medical model in Western society by making both its knowledge and value bases problematical. Clearly this exercise has all sorts of theoretical and practical implications. At the theoretical level, one's vocabulary and range of possible understandings of illness is increased by knowledge of this variety of perspectives. At a practical level, one is perhaps in a better position to evaluate the integrity of different types of therapeutic action and their significance.

One of the most important points to note is that each perspective on illness outlined above contains some kind of prescription for change or action, even if that action is simply to be more tolerant or more discerning in one's appreciation of someone else's perspective on illness (as in the case of the medical anthropological perspective) or to be more suspicious of medical intervention (as is the case with the sociological perspective). Thus each perspective presents the student with a range of possible actions, this being the ultimate point of any understanding of illness. In the end, everyone has to make practical and theoretical choices about which perspectives they are themselves going to adopt. This choice cannot be avoided, though it may be made by default. In Western society, at an 'official' level at any rate, most people opt for the medical model of illness, although, as we have seen, it is possible to maintain different models and explanations according to circumstance, place, interlocutor etc. Each perspective adopted carries with it significantly different views of responsibility, blame, causation (inner or outer), control, fate, and even of God. It also helps to determine who are to be regarded as authoritative healers and what attitude healer and sick person take to each other; in the medical model, it is the job of the healer to be active and intervene and the task of the patient to be just that. Other systems of understanding might presuppose quite different roles and relationships. For example, in theory, psychologists try to maximize their patients' own sense of responsibility for their well-being.

The practical and everyday relevance of these points may be better grasped if a fictional example is offered. A rather ill-dressed man is brought into a hospital casualty department in the middle of the night complaining of chest pains. First, it must be established what is wrong with him. Has he got a physical disorder? Perhaps he has had a heart attack? On the other hand, perhaps tests will show he has no physical symptoms. Perhaps, then, he merely thinks he is ill, in which case he may be psychologically disturbed, or he may be deliberately counterfeiting symptoms in order to get a bed for the night, or because he likes hospitals. Supposing he has indeed had a heart attack. Why has this happened? Is the cause psychological? – the man lives at a level of high tension and cannot easily relax. Or is it social? – he is unemployed and, coming from a poor neighbourhood, he has had a poor diet and little health education. Perhaps he might offer different explanations himself. Years ago, he did something very wrong; God is now punishing him for his misdoings. Perhaps he does not really think he is ill at all; he has only come to the hospital because his friends go on at him and tell him he is sick. Enough has now been said for it to be apparent that every episode of illness presents complex issues of interpretation and perspective which have to be sorted out in order that the ill person may receive the treatment he or she needs and may be referred to the right kind of healer. Hopefully, the reader now realizes that the business of identifying and treating illness is by no means as straightforward as it may seem at first sight.[54]

There is nothing theoretical about being ill or caring for a sick person. It is severely practical business. This does not mean, however, that it is not important to undertake the task of trying to understand different perspectives on illness. Illness is a mystery which eludes all of our attempts at comprehension and control. When it is presented or dealt with in a simple or one-sided way by healers of any kind, secular or religious, we can be fairly sure that it is being misrepresented. We may be being sold values, attitudes and practices which we might not want to accept uncritically, even if we accept them gratefully in certain situations of extremis. All of which serves as a prelude to examining what sort of perspectives and practices Christians are adopting in relation to illness in the contemporary world, and beyond that to some more specific issues in the elusive yet intriguing relationship between Christianity, illness and healing.

Chapter Three

Contemporary Christian Responses to Illness and Healing

The greatest achievement of Morton Kelsey's well-known study, *Healing and Christianity* (1973), is to show the way in which the institutional church withdrew its interest from the area of physical healing of the body after the first few centuries of its existence to concentrate instead on the life of the spirit and preparing people for the world to come.[1] This was the product of many different theological, physical and practical factors.

In the first place, most Christians since the Middle Ages have accepted that medical and physical means whould be the primary way of bringing about healing.[2] This implies that the role of the church is just to ensure that such means are available, hence the proliferation of Christian hospitals and missions, and that it should devote its time to giving spiritual support and consolation.

Secondly, there is the ancient idea, which predates the New Testament, that God sends sickness and uses it for his own purposes so that people either repent of their sins or are tested and strengthened in their faith (a view reminiscent of the proverb, 'Spare the rod and spoil the child'). This apparently barbarous and sub-Christian view of God which intimately links individual sin and sickness finds expression in, for example, the Order of Visitation of the Sick in the Anglican *Book of Common Prayer* of 1662:

> Wherefore, whatsover your sickness is, know certainly, that it is God's visitation. And for what cause soever this sickness is sent unto you; whether it be to try your patience for the example

of others, and that your faith may be found in the day of the Lord laudable, glorious and honourable, to the increase of glory and endless felicity; or else be sent unto you to correct and amend in you whatsoever doth offend the eyes of your heavenly Father; know you certainly that if you truly repent you of your sins, and bear your sickness patiently . . . and render unto him (God) humble thanks for his heavenly visitation, submitting yourself wholly unto his will, it shall turn to your profit, and help you forward in the right way that leadeth unto everlasting life.[3]

The third element in destroying the idea that Christians should be actively involved in physical healing using religious means was the notion of dispensationalism. This concept denotes the idea that God only performed miracles through the agency of the early church to establish it and he then withdrew this power.[4] Other ideological elements have been a growing pessimism about the value of bodily life on earth, the material dualism of modern Western thought which has emphasized the split between body and soul/mind/spirit, and more recent theologies which have rejected the notion of direct supernatural intervention in the world.[5]

On the practical level, Kelsey believes that the established, respectable, post-Constantinian church which gained worldly power and many adherents who were only semi-committed, actually lost the kind of enthusiasm and real trust in God which allowed healing to take place. All these factors are encapsulated in the fact that the Christian practice of anointing people when they were sick to effect their real bodily recovery was transformed into spiritual preparation for death in the form of extreme unction by mediaeval times. Christian healing then remained a 'spiritual' matter until the revival of interest in Christian bodily healing in the present century.

Kelsey presents the history of Christian healing as a tunnel; there is light in the early church and light in the healing revival today. In between, however, there is a thick and reprehensible darkness. At the present time, it is not really possible to over-turn Kelsey's case, for so little work has been done on the history of Christian healing methods and the attitudes of Christians to healing.[6] It is, however, possible to suggest that his presentation is somewhat one-sided and lacking in nuance.

The work of recent social historians suggests that while the institutional church may have had relatively little interest in physical healing at an official level, it has never been far from the minds of ordinary Christians facing afflictions of various kinds. The pilgrimage shrines of the saints have enjoyed a huge clientele throughout the ages on the strength of healings hoped for and gained.[7] The wells associated with religion have never lacked for sick people seeking healing.[8] Keith Thomas' survey of life in England in the sixteenth and seventeenth centuries reveals an enormous range of healers using religious or quasi-religious means to effect cures.[9]

A writer like Kelsey might object that this evidence merely witnesses to sub-Christian magical practices where healing becomes separate from the active proclamation and acceptance of the gospel. This objection can be sustained, but only if it is acknowledged that it presupposes a very particular view of Christian healing. The fact is that those who made pilgrimages to saints' tombs or holy wells presumably saw themselves as Christians resorting to religious means which would allow them to gain healing. This was the way in which God's supernatural love was made real to them. Although they did not write books or even letters setting out their theology they should not be implicitly despised or dismissed by modern writers who have very particular presuppositions about what Christian healing might be. It might well be pointed out that we do not really know what any average early Christian thought about healing or what beliefs might be operative as they witnessed the healings of Jesus or the apostles. It seems fair to conclude, however, that a real common denominator for all Christians of whatever degree of commitment at all times has been some hope that they might be physically healed by the mighty power of God operative through natural and/or supernatural means.

This discussion brings me to an important preliminary point. Just as there is no one view of illness or healing in the contemporary secular sphere, there is no one kind of Christian healing held to be such by all Christians. It is necessary to say this because the so-called Christian healing revival has become associated with very particular groups and theologies. People talk of *the* Christian healing ministry or of Christian healing in the singular. In fact, Christians are involved in healing in many ways, though many might not want to use the vocabulary of religious healing to describe their actions and beliefs. There is a tendency to see Christian healing as a monolithic entity, and indeed it is both possible and useful to identify a distinctive trend in the contemporary religious world for the sake of examination and analysis as I shall do shortly. At the same time, it is possible to accord to this self-consciously Christian perspective on healing a kind of 'moral high ground' against which all other perspectives are implicitly regarded as un-Christian or sub-Christian. This is a dangerously distorting temptation both in theory and in practice.

Most of the Christians who have ever lived have had a strong vested interest in healing of all kinds. They may well have believed in the possibility and necessity of supernatural intervention of some kind – affliction is a strong incentive to beliefs in cures of all kinds. However, they would probably have had little to do with what we might now call Christian healing. If the purpose of God in creation and the ministry to which the church is called is that of 'making and keeping human life human in the world', all kinds of activity can be called Christian healing from anointing and prayer in the ancient world, through the miracle-working shrines of mediaeval times to the medical work of seventeenth-century parish clergy to the involvement of Christian workers in the modern National Health Service.[10] As with so many other things in Christianity, it all depends on who you are and where you stand as to whether particular actions and beliefs are to be seen as Christian or not. An important question then is, 'Christian healing – says who?'[11]

One very important practical corollary of this observation is that, in most cases, the vast majority of contemporary Christians respond to illness and healing in ways which are probably indistinguishable from those of their non-Christian neighbours. That is to say that most Christians see illness and healing primarily in organic terms and seek cure from modern medical methods. Perhaps they will see a theological signficance in their disease. Possibly they may give thanks to God for the gift of modern medicine. Resort to sacraments, prayer, or any other distinctively 'religious' healing method will, however, usually be very much an accompaniment, a second thought, or, indeed, a last hope. Modern

Western Christians, like their forebears and non-believing contemporaries, are pragmatic in their responses to illness and healing. Where there are well-developed, scientifically-based and effective organic healing methods there is no need to give the supernatural or faith element in healing a prominent place. This is an important point to bear in mind as we go on to look at the so-called Christian healing revival. This is a significant development in contemporary Christianity, but it only involves a minority of Christians.

The 'Christian Healing Revival'

That the twentieth century has witnessed a revival in specifically religious healing methods as a response to illness is not in doubt. John Richards asserts that healing elements may now be encountered in up to half of English Anglican parish churches.[12] There has not been such active official and unofficial interest in this area amongst Christians in mainstream churches for centuries. Unfortunately, relatively little has been done in terms of intellectual evaluation fo the revival.[13] The field is wide open for detailed historical, sociological, theological, anthropological and medical assessments. Despite the fact that those involved in various ways with the healing revival from a number of different perspectives are themselves prolific writers they present little hard evidence of exactly who healers are, how healing actually takes place, who seeks healing by religious means and how effective that healing is.

In the face of this basic lack of evidence the assessment of the healing revival I propose here must necessarily be speculative and heuristic rather than conclusive or definitive. In the paragraphs which follow I shall first refer briefly to the history and character of what I have designated for the sake of convenience 'the Christian healing revival'. I want to emphasize that in fact there is no such single entity, but there are common strands which allow this kind of labelling to have some legitimacy. I shall then go on to assess this revival seen broadly as a whole in terms of its social, theological and practical implications.

The renaissance of explicit and intense interest in healing within the Christian churches has precisely coincided with the triumph of modern secular medicine. It might be expected that in an age where people in Western societies have never enjoyed better physical health or had available more effective medical care in time of illness that 'religious' healing would be extraneous. In fact, terms familiar in the contemporary church such as 'the Christian healing ministry' or 'the church's healing ministry' would have seemed alien to Christians living in the middle of the last century who were familiar with a continuing high mortality rate and a medical science that had yet to deliver on its promise to abolish disease and cure sickness.[14] I shall return to some possible reasons for this unlikely coincidence shortly. First, though, it is important to give a brief outline of the history of Christian healing in this century.[15]

There seem to have been two, in some ways very different, strands in Christian healing throughout the twentieth century. The first, and slightly less vociferous, is that of sacramental healing. This was represented at the beginning of the century by the foundation of the Guild of Health in 1904 by Anglo-Catholics within the Church of England. Its main thrust was and continues to be an emphasis on the efficacy of healing through the main sacraments of the church (baptism, confirmation, unction, repentance and, especially, the eucharist). This tradition continues to the present day and is well represented by people like Morris Maddocks and Christopher Hamel Cooke who tend to make much of the healing power inherent in creation and particularly witnessed to and focussed in a sacramental ministry.[16] An inevitable corollary of this emphasis on sacraments is the significance of ordained priests or ministers, for only they can duly administer the sacraments.

The second tradition which may be identified from the beginning of the century and which has had an increasing influence is that of charismatic or direct divine healing. The precise origins of this strand are obscure. However, it seems reasonable to trace them to the pentecostal revival in the United States of America which started at the end of the nineteenth century.[17] Grossly oversimplifying once again, the working assumption of this tradition is that God directly continues his miraculous healing work which began with the redeeming life and work of Jesus. Healing miracles can occur today through the intervention of God by means of prayer and actions such as the laying-on of hands. If the sacramental strand emphasizes the goodness of God in the whole of his continuing creation, the charismatic strand emphasizes the power of God in his action to redeem creation in acts of Christian healing. An important feature of charismatic healing has been the way in which it gives priority to the gifts of the individual healer and to the healing power of the Christian group met in expectant prayer rather than to the ordained ministry.[18] In fact, many of the leading exponents of divine healing have been lay people. It was one of these, J. M. Hickson, who put 'spiritual healing' on the map as far as the Church of England was concerned with his very successful healing meetings before and after the First World War.[19]

The middle and especially the latter parts of this century have seen an explosion of charismatically inspired or 'faith healing' as it is sometimes pejoratively called. It is really this which has provoked established churches to become self-consciously concerned about healing in general and the relationship between religion and medicine in particular.[20] The Institute of Religion and Medicine, set up in the early 1960s at the behest of the leaders of the religious and medical establishments, in many ways owes its existence to a not entirely admirable need to curb and critique charismatic healing.[21]

The presence of active healing ministries of all kinds also owes much of its impetus to the charismatic challenge. Official rejection or suspicion has not prevented partial imitation, even where this is not actually acknowledged. Expectations of effective religious healing have become far too widespread for major denominations to ignore them, even if they have preferred to express their interest in rather muted terms and have opted for sacramental expressions rather than those of direct charismatic intervention.[22] Doubtless Bishop Hensley Henson, who did so much to debunk 'spiritual healing', would turn in his grave to witness the distance that Anglican and other churches have travelled in this direction over the past few decades.[23] Would he or any of his peers have been able to envisage or welcome the creation of particular forms of healing service sanctioned at the highest levels by the Church of England? It seems likely that he would have regarded the revival of anointing and the laying on of hands with prayer as unwarranted and undesirable innovations into the traditional Anglicanism of the *Book of Common Prayer* which reek of a capitulation to enthusiasm and superstition. Such reservations were not shared by his episcopal successors when the Church of England authorized a book of services, *Ministry to the Sick*, in the early 1980s. Established churches, then, have travelled a long way on the impetus of the charismatic movement. Indeed, broadly charismatic attitudes to healing have become dominant in so far as religious healing events flourish, while the Institute of Religion and Medicine has suffered a steep decline in recent years.[24]

It would be impossible to give an account of all types of religious healing currently being practised here.[25] All I can hope to provide are some general points and impressions of the Christian healing movement seen as a whole. In the first place, then, methods of healing and their context vary considerably. They include the laying on of hands, anointing, prayer, and healing services (eucharistic or evangelistic). Sometimes healing is a matter of one person ministering to another in private; at others, teams of healers may work together at enormous conventions. Sometimes it is the gift of the individual healer which is emphasized, but often healing is seen to lie within the corporate body of a Christian group.

Those who exercise a healing ministry as individuals may be recognized ministers of a particular denomination, but in the case of individual charismatic healers they are quite likely to be lay people, self-authenticated by their works. In America, there is a strong tradition of evangelistic healers coming from very deprived backgrounds.[26] There is no data on the social background of such healers in this country, though it seems to be the case that healers tend not to come from the wealthiest, most powerful and well-educated strata of society.[27] People from all strata of society appear to seek religious healing, though it would again be interesting to know whether there is any social or psychological type which predominates. (If I were to speculate on this matter, I would suggest that a majority of people who seek healing come from the lower middle class in British society and below. I base this on the assumption that higher class people have greater access to health care resources, have a greater sense of their own autonomy and are generally more sceptical and less willing to surrender their autonomy to a spiritual realm. I might, however, be very wrong indeed here.)

Amongst healers, attitudes to conventional medical diagnoses and healing techniques vary considerably from a spirit of co-operation through to one of contempt. Within the arena of religious healing itself diagnosis tends to be relatively cursory; the point is not so much to know what is wrong with someone as to cure them using religious means. Explanations and diagnoses are, like those of traditional healers in other cultures, focussed on the aetiology of illness and the reason for its being present, not on detailed medical nosology. Thus MacNutt identifies sickness caused by sin, caused by past emotional hurts, caused by physical means or accidents, or caused by demonic oppression.[28] Once the proper cause has been identified, healing can follow. For the most part, healers seem relatively indifferent to the exact mechanisms by which healing is accomplished through them. There is, however, a divide between those who see their healing as a natural talent which reveals God's glory by being dedicated to him and those who see it as God's direct supernatural intervention in the world which could not be accomplished without his direct will.[29]

The common denominator which unites all those who seek religious healing is that they want to get well. Some healers think it is very important for an individual to have direct religious faith in God, others think it is enough for a person to have little faith or no faith at all, so long as there are other people around who have faith.[30] Healers of all kinds acknowledge that while healings really do take place, it is difficult to predict whether they will happen immediately and who will experience them.[31] People may be healed in different ways from those they expect. Frequently, healing is not instant. Sometimes, it may appear not to happen at all.

The types of healing which occur range from the trivial (colds, influenza, backache) to the severe (tumours, broken limbs, blindness). Sometimes healing seems miraculous or even bizarre; Gardner, for example, cites the example of South American Indians receiving fillings for their tooth cavities, each of which had a little cross on.[32] It may be external (removal of a physical infirmity) or internal (an experience of peace and removal of anxiety).[33]

Evaluating the effectiveness of religious healing methods and their success/failure rate is not possible at the present time and would be very difficult. The example of Lourdes suggests that it is an extremely problematic activity; who is to evaluate cure? Does it have to be complete and permanent or can a temporary relief of symptoms be accounted a success? Is inner healing to be regarded as healing? These questions multiply exponentially. Nonetheless, it must be recognized that much of the material which is accounted as 'evidence' for religious healing is the testimony of those who feel themselves to have been healed by religious means and it may therefore not be unbiased.[34] Factors such as the placebo effect produced by strong motivation and high expectation, as well as the possibility of spontaneous remission in illness, need to be investigated much more thoroughly.[35] Not, one suspects, that such investigations would prevent people from consulting religious healers of one kind and another, for failure is certainly acknowledged, even if its exact extent and nature are not dwelt upon to the point where they might call into question whether religious healing methods do more harm than good.[36]

For present purposes, it is unnecessary to establish whether or not religious healing methods 'work' in such a way as they could be scientifically compared with conventional medicine. The point is that many people in our society *believe* that they do, and so religious healing in general flourishes. It must be emphasized that the reason it is so prominent in both its sacramental and charismatic forms is because it is regarded as effective. Religious healing practitioners surround their activities with various theological rationales and caveats which allow them to appear to fail gracefully. In general, however, in a highly materialistic and sceptical society surrounded by sophisticated technology, they are held to be effective and that is the primary reason people go to them. They do not go for the good of their souls, they go to receive tangible bodily healing and cure. What is going on here? Why is it happening? And what are its theological and practical implications? These are questions which I now want to address more directly.

The Social Context and Implications of the Christian Healing Revival

So to the question, 'Why are we experiencing a revival of distinctively religious healing techniques, charismatic and sacramental, at a time when our physical health has never been better and when we have never before had so many effective medical techniques to promote cure in time of illness?' Religious healers, many of whom are biblicist and fundamentalist, might answer this question by simply stating that God is pouring out his healing spirit now as in the early days of the church for his own particular reasons. Perhaps, for example, he wants to bring about conversions or to re-establish the church. This answer, however, raises the question of why God ever stopped pouring out his healing spirit through the church upon the world. It also fails to do justice to the fact that manifestations of the spirit appear to be highly socially conditioned and specific. In the past, for example, the advent of spiritual healing seems to have accompanied various kinds of social unrest and protest. As these have subsided, the spirit and its attendant healings seem also to have disappeared.[37]

The first clue to the socio-cultural factors which bear upon the present revival of religious healing of all kinds is perhaps to be found in Kelsey's work.[38] It will be recalled that Kelsey saw the decline of religious healing as being closely associated with the acceptance of Christianity as the official religion of the Roman Empire. This opened the way for a church composed of individuals who had different degrees of commitment; some probably had little commitment at all. The implication of this is that the sort of spiritual enthusiasm which tends to engender and accompany religious healing is largely found in situations where Christians constitute highly motivated minority groups, or sects. The movement towards sectarianism and away from churches which embrace all the members of a particular society has been much observed by modern sociologists of religion.[39] It has gone hand in hand with a tendency for Christianity to look more overtly religious and to emphasize its closeness to its roots. Hence, there is an increase of interest in ritual and liturgy amidst mainstream denominations and a greater concern for Christian identity.[40] It is probable that the desire to emphasize distinctively religious healing reflects these trends which are having a very direct effect even on established churches, like the Church of England, which in the past have avoided religious distinctiveness, enthusiasm and extremism in commitment to ensure universality and comprehensiveness of membership.

Behind the growth of sectarian trends in churches lies the general context of secularization.[41] Broadly speaking, secularization represents the process whereby religious beliefs and institutions have lost their formal and practical influence over the main social, technological and intellectual institutions of our time. The decline in nominal church membership figures represents one aspect of secularization. The fact that churches have generally less influence in establishing and running major social institutions such as schools, universities, hospitals and the major organs of welfare provision is another.[42] Christian belief and thought systems are things into which people now have to consciously opt; many are happy to reject this option.[43]

In this context, religious healing represents an assertion of the truth of Christianity. Healings have always had a verifying function in religion. If Christianity 'works' in practical terms, it can be argued that its theological teaching is also true.[44] It also provides proof of the concrete efficacy and usefulness of Christianity in a world where technological utility is all. This encourages ordinary Christians who are anxious about the relevance of their faith. It also provides religious 'professionals' like priests, who have lost their wider influence in society, with a distinctive role. The rise of the sacramental healing revival in the early part of this century can be partially attributed to the need for priests to emphasize the distinctiveness of their own professional role at a time when they were being driven out of social welfare institutions by secular authorities.[45] A further implication of secularization and growing pluralism in society generally is that faith systems have to compete with each other. Religious healing provides an effective advertisement for the Christian faith.

Effective advertising is essential in consumerist society where people are bombarded with interesting messages from many different quarters through the mass media. A further reason, then, for the contemporary prominence of religious healing is the fact that it actually makes religion look more fascinating in a very public way.[46] Although much healing is done outside the public gaze, people are aware of the large rallies conducted by healing evangelists such as John Wimber in this country as well as in America where show business appears to pervade the religious healing scene.[47] And the business side of the show must not be underestimated. It seems doubtful that many healers make much of a living out of their work in the UK, but the techniques which they use are undergirded by huge investments in plant and manpower in the USA where healing has in fact become literally big business. A commercial, market mentality fostered by participation in a flourishing capitalist economy underlies much healing to the extent that it is often staunchly wedded to right-wing economic policies and the 'gospel of wealth'. The latter maintains that the faithful, twice-born Christian will receive positive rewards in this life and that material success will accompany conversion to Christ.[48]

The recent financial scandals surrounding American healer/ evangelists like Oral Roberts witness more eloquently than words to the the extent that healing can become bound up with the market-place. Perhaps, too, it is in the context of marketing that the interest of many healers in power should be situated. The country which gave us power selling and remains obsessed with spending power now brings us new products like power healing and power evangelism which are guaranteed to improve our material way of life even more remarkably than power detergents! The question of power is one which will be taken up theologically later on.[49]

A corollary of pointing out that healing competes directly in the market place of modern capitalist society is that Christian healing methods tend to be individualistic in their scope and operation. One of the main features of the capitalist market economy is that it emphasizes the absolute importance of the individual both as producer and consumer of goods. Mrs Thatcher articulates this explicitly when she states that there is no such thing as society, there are only individuals. But this basic attitude pervades the whole of life, including religious life where personal piety and individual religious experience are exalted over the need to develop corporate identity and a sense of social justice.[50] While religious healing methods may take place in a corporate context, they raise no awkward questions about the fundamental shape of the social order for they see illness as no more than personal sin, individual misfortune or spiritual oppression. Religious healing stays strictly in the realm of the personal and private offering personalized help to needy individuals. As such, like most medical practice, it is deeply congruent with the dominant social philosophy of our time in a way that social action for justice on the part of Christians is not.[51]

Religious healing can be seen as being in some ways an affirmation of the capitalist social order. However, it can also be seen as a protest against it, though not a revolutionary one. The warm, direct, emotional, personal and spiritual emphasis of the charismatic movement in general may be regarded as a direct response to the sense of alienation felt in all social classes because of living in a ratio-technocratic, impersonal and materialistic world. In his survey of the American charismatic movement Rifkin suggests that it is a direct response to the personal anxiety of individuals who have to cope with the disorientation induced by a rapidly changing social order.[52] The charismatic movement in general, and healing in particular, affirms the importance of the individual at a time, when, paradoxically, individuals do not seem to matter except as units of production. It helps to re-enchant and give meaning to a world from which God and the supernatural dimension have been driven out.[53] Hollenweger writes

> In certain societies the Pentecostal movement is a necessary island of humanity. For the poor it provides a home, relative economic security, care when they are sick and basic educational opportunities. It helps the managers of large factories, engineers, diplomats, artists and university professors, overloaded with responsibility, to discover the other side of their personality, the original, spontaneous and human element, and to experience it in the framework of a liturgy which controls it, but which is spontaneous in form.[54]

But, he adds,

> Whether this island of humanity enables those who visit it to make the other spheres of society more human, or whether it betrays them into shutting off the humanity that they possess from the outside world – and so losing it – is a question which in my view remains unanswered.

It will be necessary to look at the possible humanizing and dehumanizing effects of Christian healing specifically at a later point. At this juncture, however, I want to underline the fact that the charismatic movement and religious healing are not throwbacks to some better time like the apostolic age. They are phenomena of our own age.[55] More specifically, they originate in highly sophisticated, technologically advanced urban society. The coming of the Holy Spirit has more to do with urbanization and industrialization than it has to do with rediscovering the truths of the past. It may be obvious to point out that life in contemporary America is worlds away from life in first-century Palestine where healing miracles were formerly supposed to have reached their zenith. It is necessary to do so, however, lest a very particular modern vision of the past be allowed to blind us to social factors at work in the present.

A survey of the social context of contemporary religious healing could not conclude without some discussion of the relationship between this phenomenon and the practice of modern biomedicine. The power, influence and centrality of the latter has come to dominate the whole arena of physical healing in Western societies at exactly the same time as religious healing has been trying to assert itself. F. B. Smith provides a useful preface to this consideration in these words on the role of doctors in nineteenth-century Britain:

> In an age when sudden illness, disability and death threatened people at every stage of life doctors were necessary sorcerers who supplied an interpretation of otherwise meaningless afflictions . . . Doctors were taking over from the priests. They listened, diagnosed, palliated symptoms and mitigated discomfort where they could, and cured when Providence helped. The sufferer had his role of sick person confirmed. He could exhibit his individual plight to an expert auditor and observer; obtain an explanation – re-phrased in mystical words – of the condition he described in simple general language to the doctor, and a prognosis, a divination of the likely future course of his malady. This prognosis was accompanied by rituals, the inspection of faeces and urine, blood-letting, diet, nasty medicines and anti-toxins, designed to reinforce the prognosis and ensure the predicted outcome.[56]

The specifics of the passage quoted are not as important as the point that, in many ways, religion and medicine compete for the same territory. Christianity, having been driven out of the sphere of illness and healing by modern medicine, cannot reconcile itself to this exclusion. It fights back with its own battery of techniques and ideologies, correctly perceiving that one of the very important ways to a person's soul is through his or her sick body. Healing cannot be left to medical personnel. Christianity must show its continuing power and relevance, hence the evolution of a distinctive Christian healing ministry.

The basically competitive dynamic of the relationship between Christian healing methods and modern medicine is characterized by both differentiation and imitation. In so far as religious healing is undertaken by Christian believers who have no particular knowledge of specific diseases, who spend relatively little time in diagnosis, who use no technological or invasive techniques and whose vocabulary and conceptualization is essentially theological and religious, it looks as if it is completely different from medical practice. But this disguises profound similarities in the fundamental structure and outlook of both religious and medical healing.

In the first place, each hopes to offer sick people a total cure, preferably instantly (both systems fail in this aspiration, but each has mechanisms and rationales for coping with partial or total failure). Secondly, both systems regard themselves as powerful and effective, able at some level to deliver the healing which they promise. The focus of both religious and medical healing tends to be on radical intervention to cure once an illness is being experienced, rather than on preventive action to ensure continuing good health. And both these types of healing direct their attention towards the sick individual, rather than towards the social circumstances which may have made her sick.

Curiously, despite the fact that the cure of persons is the aim of both medicine and religious healing, both can be very impersonal, even de-personalizing in their operation. Such criticism is commonplace in relation to modern medicine.[57] However, religious healing can also have this quality. When, for example, the objective efficacy of a healing sacrament is emphasized, or when someone is healed by a brief encounter with a charismatic healer at a rally where they are surrounded by strangers there is an element of de-personalization. A further similarity relating to this is the decontextualization of the sick person. Much illness is treated medically by removing a person from their ordinary family and environment to place them in a hospital or surgery; religious healing also usually occurs away from a person's home or workplace, for example, at a church, at a special service, at a special healing home or, again, perhaps in hospital.[58]

An air of mystery and mystique surrounds religious and medical healing. Healers in both traditions would deny any fostering of illusion in their clients. It seems, however, that they often use the impression of superior knowledge of the unknown and special techniques to arouse the expectations of their clients and to achieve compliance and good results. Technical vocabularies, special settings for healing encounters and assurance on the part of the healer are vital accompaniments to cure.[59] Possibly the most important similarity between religious and medical healing is to be found in the asymmetrical power relationship which exists between ill people and those who try to heal them. In both cases, it is the healer or healers who is regarded as powerful and who acts while the role of the ill person consists in having faith and waiting relatively (sometimes totally) passively to see whether their illness has been driven away. For the most part, ill people are regarded as impotent in regard to their own cure and it is they who must be acted upon.[60]

It would be wrong to make too much of the similarities between religious and medical healing and it is not my purpose to discredit either by comparing them with the other. Perhaps what can be concluded from the discussion above is that certain things are necessary in any healing system if it is to be effective. It is, therefore, not surprising that religious and medical healing methods have many features in common. But the main point is that many aspects of religious healing are very similar to those which underlie the practice of modern medicine, despite the fact that, on first sight, these methods seem far apart in their methods and assumptions. This suggests that in some ways religious healing is in competition with modern medicine. It competes by aping medicine in significant ways so that it can appear to be an effective healing method itself and can gain cultural compatibility and acceptance. That I believe religious healing to be all too culturally compatible, despite the fact that, superficially, it looks like an alien throwback to ages long past when people dealt in the language of miracle more readily, will become apparent when the practical implications of religious healing are evaluated below.

Religious healing may indeed represent a new outpouring of the Holy Spirit. It may also have real elements of altruism, concern and love in action. But whatever else it denotes, it at least partly represents a bid for power and significance in the vitally important arena of health and illness on the part of marginalized Christians living in advanced industrial societies which are secularized, professionalized, indifferent and sometimes hostile. This forms an important backdrop to the theological critique which follows and attempts a partial evaluation of the religious thinking underlying the contemporary healing revival.

Religious Healing: Theological Considerations

In many ways, the Christian healing ministry which has evolved in the present century can be regarded as anti-theological or even as an anti-theology. On the whole, this area of church life has been focussed on doing something, namely trying to cure people, and not on puzzling out the theological implications of this. It is probably going too far to say that theologies of healing are all actively anti-intellectual. Nonetheless, it must be recognized that intellectual concerns and problems occupy at best a very minor place in the writings of all but a few writers on healing.[61]

This assertion can be verified by a cursory glance at the literature which has emerged from the religious healing movement in both its sacramental and charismatic forms. In general, this takes a pragmatic and apologetic line on religious issues. It is designed to exhort and encourage people to become involved in religious healing rather than to get them to ask fundamental questions about illness or about God. Most books work with a very simplistic theological framework. They show little interest in questioning what are taken to be fundamental verities, e.g., that God actively intervenes in the life of the contemporary world to heal individuals just as Jesus did in the New Testament. The emphasis lies on evangelization and motivation, not on exploration. For the most part, one could easily believe that two thousand years of dogmatic and philosophical theology had never occurred if one only had access to books on healing, for they tend to pay attention exclusively to the accounts of healings in the New Testament and to the replication of this experience in the modern world. A partial exception to this is the attention which is given to the philosophy of miracles down the centuries which is often given some prominence in more sophisticated works.[62]

The fact that much of the literature which has emerged from the modern healing revival is not intellectually sophisticated or well-informed in regard to contemporary theological concerns does not, however, mean that it is not possible to characterize the kind of theology which this movement implicitly fosters together with its methods. Nor does it preclude engaging with some of the substantive issues raised by contemporary religious healing. It is to these matters that I now turn.

It is easy to caricature the theology implicit in the healing revival as a kind of anti-theology which has little or nothing to do with the mainstream of contemporary theological discourse. In fact, this is an exaggeration. There are some important similarities and resemblances which are shared by theologies of religious healing and many other twentieth-century theologies.

In the first place, most modern theologies focus on contemporary reality; beliefs and perceptions derive their primary significance from what they can tell us about the present, not from their historical interest or the speculative information they might provide about the life hereafter.[63] Secondly, many theologies are concerned with action to change the world rather than with just understanding the world. They are praxis-oriented and have practical implications and effects; they are not just exercises in abstract intellectual formulation.[64] Thirdly, much contemporary theology is anthropocentric, that is to say, it reckons to tell us more about humanity than it does about God. Lastly, much attention is paid to the realities of the material world – heaven can look after itself, the important thing is for Christians to have an impact on the material world in which they live. And bodies are at least as, if not more, important than souls.[65]

These common factors between the implicit theological concerns and assumptions of the Christian healing movement and main themes in modern theology lead me to suggest that the former should be seen as a part of contemporary practical theology. Practical theologies, which include political and praxis-based theologies like liberation theology, black theology and ecological theology can be regarded for present purposes as places where the theological tradition is related dialectically to contemporary concerns for the sake of undertaking humanizing action for change in concrete contemporary reality.

Theologies emerging from and associated with the healing movement may have a great deal in common with practical theologies in their contemporary, anthropocentric concern for relating faith and life in healing action.[66] As yet, however, they are disappointingly attenuated and narrow. In the first place, religious healing is mostly seen as the straightforward application of ancient scriptural truths to present day conditions. There is little attempt to learn from the text of the present in order that the views and practices of the past may be critically evaluated and modified. Instead of a dialogue taking place between the realities of our knowledge about illness in contemporary society and the theological tradition, religious healing is all too often a matter of conforming the present to a very particular religious interpretation of the past.

Narrowness also characterizes the range of understandings regarded as significant and valid by healers. Unlike the liberation theologians, they do not draw widely on the resources of philosophy, theology, the social sciences or medical science to develop different practical responses and theological attitudes to different situations. What could be a very exciting area of practical theological exploration too often becomes a rut of pragmatic fundamentalism. The consequence is that important questions remain unanswered, no new insights into healing or theology emerge and new books on healing simply regurgitate the received 'truths' of the past. The whole area of healing and illness is a crucial nexus for the veracity and relevance of Christianity and Christian theology. It deserves a more active intellectual engagement than is presently offered by the religious healers themselves.

After such a preface it will come as no surprise that, on the whole, the religious healing movement has produced little fundamental theological reflection. Yet healing is surrounded by fascinating theological questions of which the following are but a few: What part does illness play within the divine providence? Is illness an evil or is it potentially a good in disguise? Can and does God use illness for his own good purposes (as the *Book of Common Prayer* implies), or is the good which may emerge from illness simply a bi-product of something which has no part in God's creation? A similar range of questions emerges in relation to healing: Are there healing powers inherent in creation or in human nature? Or do such powers come only through Christian redemption? What is to be made of 'secular' ways of healing people such as those provided by modern medicine? Are they to be regarded as direct gifts of God which should be seen as sacraments of his ongoing care in creation? Are they to be regarded as complementary or contradictory to religious healing methods?[67] All the major doctrines of the Christian faith bear upon various healing methods with their implicit notions of creation, redemption, sanctification and eschatology. But the one question which I will tackle here in a bit more depth is the question which lies both at the centre of Christian attitudes to healing and also at the centre of Christian faith, namely, what kind of God is witnessed to in this activity?

In his eloquent book, *Healing*, the American Dominican priest Francis MacNutt makes it quite clear that what is at stake in the religious healing movement is our view of the nature of God. Is God a remote abstraction who really has very little to do directly with his creation and the individuals who inhabit it? Or is he active, loving father who is known precisely by his particular benevolent interventions in the lives of his children by healing them directly in response to their faith and prayers? Indeed, how can we know that he is a loving father who cares for us personally unless he acts concretely to save us from the ravages of illness and death?[68]

At first sight, MacNutt's arguments seem both attractive and compelling. They appear to shame those apparently sceptical Christians who seem more at home with the distant God of the eighteenth-century Deists who held that God had started the world and then let it run according to its own laws and mechanisms without continuing to intervene directly in it. But perhaps the angels are not all on the side of MacNutt and other healers who use similar kinds of arguments as a theological foundation for their healing work. Might it not be the case that the only thing that is worse than a God who does *not* intervene benevolently and directly in the world, is a God who *does* intervene directly in the way MacNutt suggests? This question needs unpacking.

The main point here is that over the last few centuries Christians have come to regard the natural order as having relative autonomy from God. This may seem to have the disadvantage of marginalizing direct divine activity, but in many ways it is the only thing that allows belief in a loving God to remain possible. The thing is that if God does intervene actively in the world he is capable of preventing or averting the evils which afflict human beings. If God is omnipotent, all-loving and interventionist, why does he seem to inflict such misery on his beloved children? It may be argued that the ills which humans suffer are indeed part of God's good purpose, that they are in fact benefits in disguise. But if this is so, they do not appear to be so to those who suffer, and, in the present context this would be a contra-indicator to direct divine healing unless such healing was performed not so much for the benefit of the person healed but to accomplish some wider purpose. And if individual healing only occurs as a means to a wider end, can it be said that God truly loves and respects his children as individuals? The implication of all this is that if God can heal directly, he can prevent suffering directly, and if he is all-loving, he should indeed do so.

The interventionist God of healing miracles can also be arraigned on the grounds that he is arbitrary in his working. Healers themselves witness to the fact that not all the people who come to them are healed. Some who have great faith go away unhealed, while others who may have little faith are completely and unexpectedly healed. If God is directly responsible for this distribution of benefits, he is arbitrary to a degree which no human being could contemplate. And why, in any case, should he work to heal through very particular religious methods? An earthly loving father who had healing power would make himself available to his children in every way possible, one presumes. The fact is that the interventionist God of religious healing emerges from these arguments looking less like a loving father who is close to his creation than like an arbitrary despot who may or may not act in an overtly loving manner according to his own lights.

The issues concerning the character and being of God which are at stake in healing are those of providence and power; how does God relate to his creation? Is his providence general or specific? What sort of power does he exercise? These are complex questions which cannot be discussed fully here. In general, however, it seems wise to preserve a substantial relative autonomy for the creation and for human life. Unless this is done, God must be seen as directly responsible for all the evil in the world, human freedom must be an illusion and, as a corollary, humans have no choice about the sort of relationship and response they have to God – they are his vassals, not his lovers.

For this kind of reason, modern thinkers like Wiles and Kaufman fight shy of talking of the specific acts of God in the contemporary world, though they still leave room for people to *interpret* particular events as acts of God and they would want to affirm the necessity for human beings to continue to respond to what they know of God's love and purpose.[69] By the same token, the power of God becomes not the ability to decisively intervene in the natural order when things are going wrong, but the power to evoke a freely given loving human response to a God who reveals himself as powerless in being crucified.[70] Kaufman and McFague take this sort of thinking further in contemplating the power of human beings to destroy themselves utterly in a nuclear holocaust. The idea that God will intervene to save the human race if the crunch comes is, they suggest, a very dangerous one for it evokes a response of passivity in human hearts.[71] They argue that our ideas of God and his action in the world must change from seeing God as a powerful outsider king and lord who will always put things right to seeing him as, for example, friend, mother and lover who is alongside the human race as it struggles to respond faithfully to the creation of its own destiny in the freedom which it has been given by God.[72]

We may now seem to have travelled a long way from MacNutt's simple and apparently hopeful assertion that God's sovereign and fatherly love for his children is being manifested directly and anew by the occurrence of divine healing on earth in the present time. It may be that MacNutt is right in his assertion and that the wider context which I have sketched in is an irrelevant one. I want to make it clear that I do not in any way want to deny that people are healed by religious means. I hope, however, that the arguments I have outlined make it clear that the attribution of healing directly to the divinity may be a false or dubious one which raises more problems than it solves on both theoretical and practical levels.

Theologically, it brings up issues of theodicy, providence and the nature of God. It also requires us to answer yet again the fundamental question, 'What is the nature of the Christian God and in what sense can he in fact be said to be healing in the world today?' Practically, problems are raised about the way in which Christians should witness to the healing power of God and types and degrees of human responsibility in the arena of illness and healing. Does healing come from on high at particular moments through the direct action of a sovereign God? If so, let religious healing services and sacramental acts multiply. If, on the other hand, healing is seen as an essentially intra-worldly phenomenon which is primarily a human responsibility exercised by followers of a powerless, crucified God, witness may take a very different form. It might, for example, be important to become a great deal more concerned about the whole world in which we live and of the sources of harming and healing within it – and us.

In this section I have tried to outline the theological nature and context of religious healing and some of the questions which emerge from it. It has not been my intention to 'knock' religious healing methods, nor the theology which is implicit in them. I have simply tried to point out how theologically impoverished this area is and how much it needs more critical assessment and dialogue if it is to be faithful to its laudable and practical task. I move on now to provide a partial critique of religious healing attitudes and methods as a whole.

A Critique of Contemporary Christian Responses to Healing and Illness

In this final part of the chapter I want to offer some fairly trenchant criticisms of Christian responses to healing and illness in general. These will be of particular relevance to the movement dedicated to distinctively religious healing methods which has been discussed in the main body of the chapter. They are, however, relevant to all contemporary Christian responses, whether they are of pragmatic apathy or revivalist enthusiasm.

Usually, I think of criticism as essentially evaluative so that it weighs both positive and negative features of any subject under consideration. In the present instance, however, my criticism is of a generally negative kind. Christian healing responses to illness are mostly born of an enormous sense of urgent and positive practical conviction; the case *for* various ways of responding to illness has been put very eloquently and vociferously many times before. Here, I want to point up some of the areas of omission and doubtful validity which, I suggest, Christians concerned about healing and illness should begin to address.

Before I start on my criticisms, let me re-iterate that any method or attitude which actually alleviates human misery and distress would seem to have a *prima facie* right to be regarded as a good thing; it seems very likely that religious healing methods do accomplish real relief and cure of illness. The point is that a much more vigorous evaluation is needed of these methods, attitudes and the values that they promote in order, as the moral philosophers might put it, that good may be done and evil may be avoided. I offer the criticisms which follow as a starting point for deeper reflection and response, not in a spirit of hostility or destructive animosity.

The first and over-arching criticism to be made here is precisely that Christian responses to healing and illness are made *uncritically*. I have already explored the way in which, for example, the sort of healing promoted by charismatic healers contains within it the concept of a directly interventionist God which raises all sorts of complex theological problems. This sort of uncritical attitude to theology and belief is repeated many times over in all parts of the Christian response to healing; people seize on a set of simple beliefs, e.g., people can only be healed through the use of 'God-given' modern medicine, and then they apply them consistently to all circumstances.

The area of healing really ought to be an area of exciting theological dialogue, a place where different beliefs and practices collide and enter into creative dialogue with each other. This would not only ensure that Christians actually learned about their faith from the experience of dealing with illness, it would also ensure that ill people were not subjected simply to the ideological preferences of one particular world view. What people believe affects how they act in the world. It is, therefore, very important that what they believe is subjected to scrutiny so it is apt and true in the circumstances of encountering illness.

Christians are not merely uncritical in relation to their beliefs and theology in the area of illness and healing. They are uncritical about the effects of their response, both intended and unintended. In secular medical circles these days, it is customary to conduct clinical trials on any new form of drug or other treatment. This ensures that the new treatment is sufficiently beneficial that it justifies widespread usage. It may well be objected that God should not have to enter a therapeutic trial by people conducting scientific tests on those who have been subjected to religious healing. Perhaps this would not be the best way of ensuring that people benefit from religious healing in any case. But there would seem to be a good case for healers trying to assess the real value of their work beyond merely collecting testimonials from their satisfied clients. In many spheres it often turns out that therapeutic methods are less effective than their administrators think they are.[73]

Responsible healing surely demands some attempt at real assessment, even if it does not go to the lengths which are insisted upon by those examining miraculous cures at Lourdes. It may be that far fewer people benefit from religious healing methods than is thought by religious healers. More seriously than that, there may be people who are in fact harmed by their encounters with religious healing. Running alongside the testimonies of those who have been helped by religious methods in one way or another is a much more worrying set of stories about people who feel that their hopes have been dashed, that they failed to recover from illness because they had not had enough faith or because they were in the grip of some deep and nameless sin. Such people learn despair and a sense of abandonment by God from their encounters with religious healing.

If there are more of them than there are people who feel that they have been helped, there is a strong case for changing beliefs and practices in Christian healing as well as for ceasing to practice religious healing altogether.

Just because you do something in the name of a good and loving God does not mean that you are God, nor that what an ill person experiences, as a result of your actions, is the goodness and love of God. Medical practitioners, counsellors and other carers now have to face and evaluate the fact that they do harm as well as help.[74] Hoping for the best and trusting in the Lord is not enough anymore. Two questions which might usefully be remembered in encountering any religious healing response are: (1) How do we know that this does not harm people? and (2) What measures are taken to ensure that if people are harmed they do not lose the sense of a loving God who remains present with them no matter what?

A second criticism of contemporary Christian responses to illness and healing is that they often seem highly *anachronistic*. A reading through books about healing and liturgies for healing services, even if they were written last year, transports the reader back into the cultural world of the New Testament. Illness is due to sin, or the wiles of demons; it is cured by methods sanctioned by the early church such as anointing and laying on of hands.

It may indeed be the case that the old ways are the best ways. Methods which have a close superificial affinity to those of the early Christians may have a timeless value. These assumptions, however, need to be looked at much more carefully, especially in the light of the fact that for so many centuries the church coped admirably without what are now deemed to be central planks of the healing ministry. As we saw above, the religious healing revival is a response to modernity not a simple continuation of the methods of antiquity. A marginalized church seeks to gain strength and identity for the present and so turns sharply towards some aspects of the tradition of the past, in this case, certain views and practices of healing. There is certainly nothing wrong with turning to the past for inspiration or confirmation of desirable present-day practices (though there may be some self-deceit involved in trying to pretend that, just because there were particular responses and ideas in the past, these should be exactly imitated today). It seems rather depressing, however, that contemporary Christians seem determined not to acknowledge that the world has changed radically over the last two millennia or to develop their own original responses to illness and healing today.

In many ways, sacramental and divine healing methods represent innovations of the last century legitimated by some correspondence with ancient tradition. It would not seem wrong for believers in a God who makes all things new and who does new things in the world rather than being captured in the first century, to think of imaginative new ways of being engaged in illness and healing today. It seems utterly ridiculous that the form of laying on of hands and anointing adopted by a major denomination like the Church of England in the 1980s should give no hint (beyond the actual words it uses) that it is a product of a modern world where there are institutions like hospitals and developments like technologically based medicine. To attempt timelessness in responding to illness is to ensure contemporary irrelevance. To cleave to the assumptions and practices of the past, just because they come from the past, is to stifle imagination for the present and future.[75]

The third criticism is like unto the second. This is that Christian responses to healing and illness have been incredibly and unduly *narrow*. The last chapter revealed the variety and complexity of different ways of looking at illness, and of course, that each different way of looking at illness requires a slightly different response in terms of prevention or healing. Little of this breadth and depth of different perspectives is evident in Christianity. For Christians all illness is illness; it can be understood in a restricted number of ways, e.g., as misfortune, as demon oppression or as the result of sin. It can be dealt with religiously in correspondingly few simple ways, e.g., prayer, exorcism, laying on of hands, anointing. Now there are Christians who consider themselves to be living on a religious island in the middle of a pagan sea and who therefore feel that they should have nothing to do with the ways or understandings of things like the medical or social sciences, nor with their methods of healing. Most people, including presumably the liturgical committees of major Christian denominations, do not take this line. There is much they could learn about healing and illness from outwith religious understandings. It is time that this learning was fostered so that more imaginative and nuanced responses are made to what is known of the contemporary realities of illness and healing.

Holding strange, idiosyncratic beliefs within a mystical enclave, where magical-looking rites are conducted from time to time, should certainly not be the only valid way of expressing Christian faith and healing concern in an age which knows so much about the causes and responses to disease. Indeed, the practice of distinctively 'religious' healing methods, insofar as it does appear to be the manipulation of the supernatural for the benefit of suffering humanity (and of course that is why suffering humanity resorts to it – let us not be deceived about that), may be an obstacle to a more complex, more difficult and more authentic witness to healing.

It may be thought that here I am covertly trying to disparage 'religious' healing based on churches, theology and liturgical methods for the sake of exalting non-religious healing methods and perceptions. In a sense this is true, but only if it is held that God acts mainly or exclusively through the church. My point is that truly religious responses are those which are sensitive to God's ongoing work in the whole of creation and through all people. One of my main anxieties about religious healing is that it takes far too narrow a view of religion. Ironically, it seems to me that in taking this kind of narrow view Christians actually allow the world to write an agenda for them insofar as they allow social trends such as secularization to push them into very limited concerns, world views and practices.

The last point about present Christian patterns of responding to illness and healing obscuring the need to develop more complex and costly healing responses, brings me to my last criticism. The majority of Christian responses had been *individualistic and socio-politically naive* to the extent that sickness may even have been multiplied. Some of the most significant and devastating findings about the causes and incidence of illness over the last two centuries have centred on the fact that social circumstances have a consider-able influence in determining who becomes ill, what sort of illnesses they get and what sort of healing facilities are then offered to them. The Black Report, *Inequalities in Health*, reveals consistent relationships between social class position and ill health.[76] The lower down the social scale one is, the poorer health one enjoys and the less access one has to caring facilities. Findings like these project the whole business of disease and healing into the social and political realm. They also raise profound questions about social structure and social justice.

With a very few honourable exceptions, this whole area has been ignored in Christian thinking and practice.[77] A service such as the Church of England's order for laying on of hands and anointing focusses only on the sick individual when she has already become ill. It says nothing about the need for the prevention of illness. Although it allows the individual to confess her sins it provides no way of recognizing that, in many ways, her illness might be the product of unjust social circumstances. So a woman who has been a smoker and now has lung cancer goes through an act of repentance and is anointed. But what of the company which encouraged her to smoke in the first place to enhance its profits (working-class women are a prime target for cigarette-company propaganda and are amongst the largest group of smokers now in our society)? And what of the society which allows the company to advertise its products with considerable freedom? Where does the need for repentance really lie, and how is society going to be healed of its sin?

Christian healing, like much medical healing, makes the sick individual its object and concern. Illness is divorced from social structures. It can only be cured not prevented. It is a personal misfortune and has nothing to do with principles of justice. Indeed, in taking this general line Christianity actually reinforces the idea that illness is a personal matter which cannot be prevented and so passively supports the prevailing social order, whatever its cost in terms of widespread suffering throughout society.

Once again, it has to be said that this blinkered attitude will not do. If we know that some things in society promote illness, it is surely better to engage in preventative action rather than reactive healing. Of course, it is true that there will always be sick individuals who require an individualized Christian healing response. Such responses should, however, be situated within a search for justice and healing in society as a whole, as a response to the God who expresses his love in justice as well as in acts of individual care. It is very difficult to contemplate what a socio-politically informed structural healing response might look like in practice. Contrast the ease with which we are able to think of and talk of individualized responses – individualism really does pervade our whole mentality (another case of the world writing the agenda for Christians perhaps?). It would almost certainly mean becoming actively informed about and involved in the grey world of politics, social structures and competing interests and it might well be more costly and lack the personal gratification of personal healing ministry. But if Christians are not prepared to evolve a healing ministry on this level their individualized healing responses will continue to contribute to the ideology of injustice. They will be proclaiming peace where there is no peace. To this extent, they may be distorting the full gospel.

The remaining chapters of this book, and especially the last one, are written very much with these criticisms in mind. In the next chapter I explore themes of politics and conflict in illness and healing. These ideas are concretized to a greater extent by examining potential Christian responses to mental illness in the following chapter and my concluding consideration of AIDS.

Chapter Four

Politics, Conflict, Healing and Illness

A concept which has come to be closely associated with the Christian concern and quest for healing and health is that of 'wholeness'.[1] Wholeness is sometimes even equated with healing – 'Healing is wholeness', it is asserted. I have several objections to this association and usage. In the first place, to describe healing as wholeness is to define one vague concept in terms of another which is equally vague. Secondly, as a matter of practical observation, it often seems to be the case that healers and, indeed, healthy people are far from being whole. Consider many of the great saints of history who manifested the Christian ideal in their respective generations and brought healing to many, but who remained deeply damaged at many levels and often had a profound contempt for their own well-being; John Wesley and Francis of Assisi would be two such people. In the present context, the primary objection to the prominent use of 'wholeness' as a leading concept in considering illness and healing is that it tends to trivialize, spiritualize and to make ethereal what appear to me to be the real struggles and conflicts which surround and express themselves in illness and healing.

I take wholeness to designate, *inter alia*, reconciliation, peace, joy, the integration of opposites, and complete harmony of body, mind and spirit, as well as unity within and between individuals and communities at all levels. As such, wholeness is certainly something to be desired and actively pursued. The trouble is that such an elusive and imprecise ideal is not to be found in a world which is divided and shattered in so many ways. In the context of the fragmented reality we have to endure this concept can sound like, and serve as, hollow ideology, 'pie in the sky when you die'. It lacks concrete proposals or directions. It may encourage Christians to opt for a vague future dream rather than trying to enter into the real contradictions, conflicts and political ambiguities which are an integral part of the quest for healing in a broken and complex world.

In this connection, I am tempted to suggest that wholeness is a concept which is only really used by those of us who are so far removed from the real fight for health and healing in daily life that we can claim to see the world in terms of ideal universal patterns rather than in terms of the very unsatisfactory specifics provided by the 'worm's-eye view'. Where precisely does talk of 'wholeness' fit in to the daily reality confronted by patients and staff in an underfunded National Health Service, for instance? And what is the real value of the term for the dispossessed peoples of the world who suffer most from the diseases and disorders of the present time?

In his classic *Plagues and Peoples*, William McNeill situates human life in the midst of a bloody struggle against two kinds of threat. On the one hand, there are fellow human predators. On the other, there are the threats posed by natural enemies such as disease.[2] Throughout history, life has been determined in a very large measure by conflicts between human groups and individuals and by the struggle against disease. It is not for nothing that we talk of 'fighting' disease and that military metaphors abound in everyday medical life. Consider, for example, the *triumphs* of modern medicine.

The underlying aim of this chapter is to explore some aspects of conflict and politics in the search for healing. It attempts to redress any temptation there may be amongst Christians to ignore these very real dimensions in the name of some vague, anodyne notion of wholeness. Using historical and contemporary resources, I want to draw Christian concern for healing away from the search for some kind of idealistic harmony and consensus. I would like to invite Christians to take more seriously the contradictions, conflicts and power struggles, both implicit and explicit, which surround and always have surrounded illness and healing. If at times I may overdraw my case in this regard, it should be remembered that I do this to counter a trend in churches to completely de-politicize and harmonize the area of healing. In theological terms, this is an outworking of the belief that reconciliation, harmony and healing cannot ultimately be achieved by ignoring the dimensions of power and conflict but only by engaging in them.

In practical terms, I hope readers will want to reassess the context of their healing concern, and that they will become more engaged in the small but important skirmishes in the battle or struggle for healing, rather than standing on the olympian mountain of 'wholeness' from which standpoint the particular engagements of the battlefield blend into a distant, tasteful, aesthetically pleasing and harmonious pattern.

Conflict, Politics and the Healing Ministry of Jesus

The dimensions of conflict and politics in healing and illness first impinge on Christianity in the ministry of Jesus. Jesus' healings are often presented as simply acts of individual kindness undertaken towards afflicted individuals for motives of personal compassion. This kind of interpretation need not be dismissed in its entirety. It is necessary, however, to place the healing ministry of Jesus within a much broader social and political context than has hitherto been popular.

Contemporary New Testament scholars like Sanders and Theissen using historical and sociological methods provide valuable new insights into the situation of Roman-occupied Palestine which forms the backdrop to Jesus' ministry.[3] Their researches reveal a situation of considerable social dislocation and disruption in Palestine in general, and Galilee in particular. Many people were being driven from the land and their social roots to become relatively poor and dispossessed:

> At the time of Jesus there were many socially rootless people in Palestine. Many lived in unconscious readiness to leave their ancestral homes. They included the disciples of Jesus. But these represented only a variant of possible behaviour. Anyone who was dissatisfied with things as they were could become a criminal or a healer, a beggar or a prophet, a man possessed or an exorcist. He could identify himself with a new form of Judaism or lose his identity completely and become a helpless victim of 'demons'.[4]

Theissen situates the ministry of Jesus and the lives of his first followers firmly within the sector of Palestinian society which was excluded from power and riches. The first followers of Jesus were disillusioned and deeply critical of the rich and powerful, hence the trenchant criticism in the Gospels of those who had money and influence. They were drawn to Jesus, amongst other prophets and visionaries, because of his teaching about a Kingdom of God in which earthly values would be reversed. They were looking for a better future.

Times of social crisis and disruption have often formed the background to the emergence of visionary teachers and healers who present an attractive eschatological vision, and who are able therefore to command influence over mass audiences.[5] The social circumstances of Palestine, then, must be seen as an essential part of the impetus for Jesus' ministry in general and for his healing ministry in particular. Healings provided validation for the message of the preacher and were necessary signs of better things to come.

This basic perception can be amplified by underlining the context of Jesus' healings within his preaching of the Kingdom of God. This term can never have been devoid of real social and political connotations, even if it is now difficult to discern that Jesus' followers would have understood by it precisely. Contemporary Palestinians were drawn to Jesus because of his vision of a better social order where the poor and the outcast would have a prominent place and where injustices would be rectified. The healings acted as a draw and a confirmation of the truth of the proclaimed message and the authenticity of the messenger.[6]

At this point, something must be said about the way in which spiritual or divine healers use their unusual powers to commend themselves and their message to both followers and sceptics alike. In the history of religions world-wide, it is a well-recognized phenomenon that those without worldly power or influence claim to be inspired by a spirit or spirits beyond themselves which allow them to exert power themselves and to challenge the power structures which surround them.[7] There can be no doubt that Jesus was perceived as charismatically inspired. He probably saw himself in this light, too; compare the coming of the Holy Spirit at his baptism.

Whatever the reality of the latter speculation, it does not seem over-inventive to suggest that Jesus' charismatic ministry of healing was an assertion of power and influence at an informal level outwith the main social power structures of the day. In this sense, it is difficult not to conclude that Jesus' healings were overtly political in that they were part of an (unconscious?) bid for power and influence even if they were only implicitly confrontational. The healings certainly contributed to the collection of followers around Jesus and it was this following which probably contributed to his being recognized as a significant political threat to the extent that he was arrested and executed after his far more overtly confrontational action of cleansing the Temple in Jerusalem.[8]

The social, political and conflictual dimensions of Jesus' healing ministry are further highlighted by the fact that the healings seem to have caused much controversy amongst those who witnessed them and by recalling the conflictual language in which healings, and more particularly exorcisms, are described. As far as we can discern, Jesus appears to have seen himself as being involved in a war against Satan and his Kingdom in the name of the Kingdom of God. It may be that much of the language of war which we use today of the struggle against illness finds its ultimate source in the healings of Jesus. He certainly seems to place healing in a combative light.

At this point I want to draw attention to the insights given by R. A. Lambourne into the healing works of Jesus.[9] Far from seeing these as revelations of individually-orientated compassion (What about all the people who were presumably not healed by Jesus?), Lambourne suggests that the healings should be seen primarily as social events which had primary significance for communities rather than individuals. Lambourne argues that they were signs of a socio-political entity, the Kingdom of God. In a way, then, the healings were acted parables. They provoked a response from those who witnessed them and they would be deeply divisive of communities. Some could only see in Jesus' healing the finger of Satan or Beelzebul (Jesus' putative possessing spirit).[10] Others recognized an inbreaking of the Holy Spirit and chose life, health and healing for themselves and their communities. In this way, the healing functioned as concrete judgment of the Kingdom on actual earthly communities. This challenging, judging and social aspect of the healings produced much controversy. Once again, it may be seen as part of the precipitating circumstances which ultimately led to the rejection and execution of Jesus.

As a child, I sometimes used to sing a hymn which began, 'Jesus' hands were kind hands, doing good to all'. I cannot now remember the words which followed, but I can testify to the sort of view they gave me of Jesus. They presented him as a benevolent, Father Christmas-like, proto-general practitioner whose one desire was to help people to get better as individuals. In this brief account I hope I have succeeded in modifying this view of Jesus' healing ministry by suggesting that Jesus' ministry was not unrelated to social factors, particularly social disintegration, that his person, message and technique was strongly influenced by the society and times of which he was a part, that his message and ministry had substantial socio-political content and implications (even if these are now hard to define precisely) and that his healings must be seen against a background of protest and controversy. In some ways, indeed, they can be seen as heightening protest and controversy. Ultimately, everything in Jesus' ministry, including his healings, must be seen in the light of his execution by the political authorities. The healings cannot, then, be divorced from the wider themes of political and social order, power and powerlessness and fundamental conflict.

In advancing this view, which is based at least to some extent on reputable recent New Testament scholarship, it is not my intention to suggest that because Jesus' ministry had a particular form and emphasis, contemporary concern should be concerned to imitate it exactly. All I want to do is to reclaim aspects of Jesus' healing ministry from the realm of a-political, de-contextualized and individualized benevolence and good will whence it has been exiled so firmly by many Christian practitioners and writers on healing. In fact, there is an urgent need to perform the same kind of exercise in relation to the whole of the healing tradition. Social context, power relations and conflict need to be written back in. Only thus can these elements come to seem less alien to Christians concerned about healing today so that they can exercise a broader and more discriminating healing ministry. In the sections which follow it will be possible to do this to a very limited extent and to develop more broadly some of the perceptions identified in relation to Jesus.

Illness and Healing as Power and Protest

I now want to spend some time developing the apparently unlikely notion that both illness and healing can be seen as being deeply involved in issues of power, control and protest. I would not argue that they are *always* involved in this way. I would, however, certainly want to assert that the possibility of this kind of dimension being present should be borne in mind when assessment is made of any incidence or pattern of illness or healing. An important presupposition for this consideration is that both healing and illness are often covert ways of engaging in power relationships. On the face of it, the ill person is an involuntary victim of forces outwith his or her control. S/he is seen as a sufferer. By the same token, the healer is perceived as a benevolent reliever of suffering, a doer of good. I hope to show that these views of illness and healing are, in some situations at least, naive. They may sometimes conceal a very important, if only covertly articulated, dialogue about power and social control.

It is not difficult to substantiate the idea that healing has much to do with power and protest. The mighty works of Jesus have already been considered. There can be no doubt that these did much to confirm his authority as a teacher and leader. Those perceived to be healers in every society down the ages have been accorded great power and authority which stems ultimately from close contact with the forces of chaos and death which both threaten and energize the social order.[11] In our own society, doctors are given undue power and influence on all kinds of issues, not merely because they have received an expensive and technical education, but because their activity is bound up with life-threatening forces. Though few medical practitioners would want to claim charismatic power, many are effectively accorded it by those in need, i.e. by most members of the population. This charismatic influence can be used by doctors not only to command large rewards for their work, but also as a platform for wider political influence. So, for example, the public is more likely to be influenced by doctors protesting about nuclear weapons than they might be by clergy or hospital porters. This occurs despite the fact that there is no reason to suppose that the latter groups should not be at least as well informed and involved as their medical counterparts. The medical profession in our society commands the social heights partly through its institutionalized and routinized appropriation of charisma.[12]

A relatively large, formally trained and publicly recognized medical profession, which monopolizes healing power by force of law, is largely associated with the rise of industrial societies and of Western biomedicine. In the past, ways of acquiring the power associated with healing have been more informal. From the point of view of the Christian tradition and of pre-literate societies an important way of becoming a healer was to have a direct and personal experience of being possessed by a 'good' spirit. In his research on shamans (inspired charismatic healers in traditional societies), the social anthropologist I. M. Lewis has identified a pattern whereby, typically, a person falls ill (is possessed by evil spirits) but eventually recovers and is then aided by those same spirits in curing others (he becomes a master of spirits).[13]

This pattern is frequently found in the Christian healing tradition. Indeed, it can be postulated of Jesus' own healing career. It will be recalled that Jesus had the experience of being entered by the spirit at his baptism and that he then underwent severe trials in the desert. Out of this experience he then emerged as a healer and teacher, but there was a great deal of debate amongst his contemporaries as to whether he was possessed by the good holy spirit or by another spirit, Beelzebul.[14] By acquiring supernatural powers from outside himself, the healer becomes confident of the legitimacy and authority lying behind his work. He can challenge earthly and supernatural authorities and powers with confidence and impunity. It is within this kind of context of the supernatural acquisition and legitimacy of power that healing can often be seen as an incentive to, or confirmation of social protest or power. This can be graphically illustrated from the socially troubled history of seventeenth-century England.

One of the ways in which Stuart kings established their divine right to rule was by virtue of their consecration at their coronation. This did not confer merely temporal power, but also the power to heal by touching people with scrofula (the so-called 'King's Evil'). In the turbulent years of the Civil War, one of the ways in which Puritan extremists who wanted to overthrow the monarchy could exhibit a counter legitimacy for their own social reforms was by also being able to heal by touch, the implication being that healing in this charismatic way directly indicated divine favour of the healer and his cause. Of course, a greater success rate in healing than that managed by other healers implied even greater legitimacy for a cause, hence there were extensive debates about the actuality of healings and their possibility. One Puritan 'stroker', Valentine

Greatrakes, nearly got into very severe trouble with the authorities in the time of Charles II because his activities were seen as a direct challenge to the King and, by implication, to the legitimate social order as a whole.[15]

Other, more flamboyant, figures can be mentioned. George Fox, the founder of Quakerism, who expounded a radical form of religion and life also performed many miracles.[16] Significantly, perhaps, his followers destroyed his *Book of Miracles* shortly after his death. Part of the motivation for doing this was probably to make the new religious movement appear less threatening to the dominant religious and secular powers so that Quakers could enjoy greater tolerance and equilibrium. Moving into the eighteenth century, John Wesley was famous for his miracle-working and exorcisms. Our own century has witnessed the establishment of many black and evangelical sects on the basis of an ability to cure the sick which is held to denote divine favour and the legitimacy of the gospel being preached.

The conclusion which may be reached on this cursory review of some historical evidence about charismatic healing is that there is nothing like getting God overtly on your side if you wish to change society or found a new religious movement. If you lack secular power or the means to obtain it, the Holy Spirit provides a short cut to considerable influence which may allow you to challenge the powers that be at the highest levels. There is no quicker or more concrete way of God showing that he has put his power at your disposal than by being able to heal people. This reassures any followers who might waver and ensures their continued interest and commitment; everyone needs healing for themselves or their kin sooner or later. At the same time, healing can be held up to outsiders as an unequivocal good. It really does look very churlish indeed if those in power, particularly religious people in a 'Christian' country, try to suppress or cast aspersions on a group or individual who only heals people. The legitimacy of their own position is brought into question by such sceptical or damning attitudes.

In this way, healing can become a battleground between social groups, especially those who have a great deal of social power, influence and control and those who have none. It is not an accident that many contemporary charismatic healers in the pentecostal tradition come from the poorer classes or from ethnic minorities which are excluded from the main stream of social recognition and influence. Only by appropriating the spirit directly can such people gain significance in the world.[17] Similarly, it is not surprising that those in positions of worldly power and control are often indifferent or hostile to healing gifts of the spirit. They can get their way in society and in terms of health care by other means.

A healer may be seen as controversial and the legitimacy of his methods and message may be questioned, but it is relatively easy to see that any kind of healing is active and powerful and so can form the basis for protest and control. It is, perhaps, not so easy to see illness in this light. Illness is primarily experienced as an unwanted alienating phenomenon which deprives people of power over their lives and those of others. But does it really do this in all circumstances? Perhaps these are types of illness and situations in which the power of the supposed victim is in fact enhanced. It is not uncommon to hear psychologists talk of 'secondary gain' in relation to various types of human behaviour. By this they mean that, on the face of it, a person may be a suffering victim of events outside his or her control, but that there may be features of their situation which they may regard as positive or desirable. This perception can be amplified by referring back to the sociological understanding of the sick role outlined in chapter 2 above.[18] It will be recalled that a person who is designated as sick is relieved of normal responsibilities and duties. Those around people perceived to be occupants of the sick role are obliged to look after them until they recover from their illness. The roles of sick person and carer are predicated on the notion that the sick person does not will his or her own condition, that its causes lie outwith his/her control, and that he/she actively desires to recover.

If the psychological and sociological theorists are correct, it may be possible to identify examples of situations where people who have little control and influence in ordinary life actually gain these things by becoming ill. Of course, they cannot simply simulate illness or they are designated as malingerers and given short shrift. But the possession of a real illness (which must be seen as possession *by* an illness) may open up real possibilities of personal control and protest which cannot be achieved by any other means.

Not surprisingly, this insight has been principally vindicated by studies of women's experience of illness, and particularly mental and mentally-related illness. In almost all societies on the face of the earth, women are relatively powerless. In his studies of traditional societies, I. M. Lewis has identified a pattern of 'possession' whereby women can register a clear but covert protest against the injustices of the social order in which they find themselves dominated by men without overtly subverting that order.[19] Such women are taken over by evil spirits until such time as they receive the attention and gifts which they desire from their husbands. At that point, they are then exorcised. Lewis stops short of identifying this ecstatic, trance or possession experience with our notion of mental illness, though it looks very similar and provides instructive parallels. He describes such protest as 'an oblique aggressive strategy', which is a gesture of defiance but also one of hopelessness and acceptance of the status quo.[20]

The historian Rudolph Bell has no hesitation about describing aspects of the religious experience of some of the female Italian saints of the Middle Ages as anorexia nervosa.[21] Bell suggests that becoming anorexic, or controlling oneself and one's physical appetites, allowed religious young women to escape the domination of men and to gain some autonomy in their existence in that it allowed them to break with family life and expectations. He traces the process whereby the virtuous 'holy anorexia' came later to be regarded as demon possession and was then transmuted into pathology and illness. By the seventeenth century, sanctity was expressed in good works, not in extreme bodily privation.

Roy Porter identifies a similar process of women using unusual or pathological experience to free themselves from the domination of men. His prize example is Margery Kempe, the English mediaeval mystic, who was able to relinquish the duties of marriage and family life on the strength of her direct and extraordinary religious experience. This sounds suspiciously like a nervous breakdown to the modern reader.[22]

The use of what we might call illness to gain power and control over one's destiny is not confined to interesting but obscure historical examples. Readers will be familiar with well-known historical figures who have 'enjoyed' ill health. Elizabeth Barrett Browning is an example here. They may have actually encountered people who appear to gain a great deal of power and attention from having an illness. Perhaps phobias are the best contemporary example; the person who cannot leave his house because of illness requires a great deal of attention and support from others – why should he want to be cured? Some recent writers on depression emphasize the fact that, in a real but perhaps obscure sense, those who are depressed chose to lock themselves in a prison because of the secondary gains it provides.[23] Whatever the truth of this assertion, it emphasizes the fact that an illness may be an important if distorted attempt to gain influence over one's own destiny in the only way one can. As such, it may represent a form of protest, albeit a muted and relatively ineffective one. The idea that some illness may function in this way should not, however, be allowed to hide the fact that most illness is genuinely unsought and represents unfortunate affliction rather than a desire to control or be heard.

The purpose of this section has been to point out some of the ways in which both illness and healing can participate in conflict and struggles for personal and social control in particular social settings. This is all part of a general point; there is often more to healing and illness than first meets the eye. Healing is frequently the genuine exercise of benevolent and altruistic power to relieve affliction. Illness may be nothing more than straightforward bodily infection. Neither healing nor illness, however, should be seen as totally isolated from social context and potential struggles for influence and control.

Some of the theoretical and practical implications of this perspective for contemporary Christians in relation to contemporary health services and healing encounters will be developed in the last two sections of this chapter, but I turn now to some of the power, control and conflictual aspects of the relationship between the church and the medical profession over the centuries.

Conflict, Religion and Medicine

The Institute of Religion and Medicine set up under the auspices of the president of the Royal College of Physicians and the Archbishop of Canterbury in the 1960s embodies the principle which is widely held amongst liberal Christians, namely that their religion and contemporary medicine have a great deal in common. From one perspective, historically, this principle is absolutely correct. Religious and medical practitioners share the distinction of being members of the oldest professions on earth. There can be no doubt about the significance which Christianity in particular

has attached to illness and healing; one fifth of the gospel accounts
of the ministry of Jesus is taken up with accounts of his healings.
Readers will be familiar with the long tradition of both 'secular' and
'spiritual/sacramental' healing and care which has been associated
with the history of the church. The former has been expressed in
various kinds of medical skill and in the provision of hospice and
hospital care. The latter has spawned healing miracles at the tombs
of saints, as well as various types of spiritual intervention and
concern.

The centrality of healing to both medicine and Christianity,
then, is not in dispute. But in this section I want to dwell a little
on the real conflicts, tensions and power struggles which have
characterized the relationship between medicine and Christianity
down the centuries. This relationship has not had mill pond-like
calm which modern proponents of medico-religious dialogue and
co-operation are wont to emphasize. Indeed, it has often been very
stormy and hostile. I want to suggest that this kind of perspective
should put a question mark against an idealistically harmonious
view of the relations between religion and medicine today.

Although we know very little about early Christian attitudes to
medicine it seems that, from the start, Christianity seems to have
had an ambivalent attitude to curing illness using natural or proto-
scientific means such as those developed in the Greek medical
tradition of Hippocrates. Possibly this stemmed from basic perceptions of the meaning of illness. Christianity recognized that illness
could come from divine, evil or natural sources. It was always
important to try to discern the wider purpose and meaning of an
illness rather than simply trying to eradicate it, for God might be
trying to communicate something through it. It was equally
important that the right means should be used to effect cure. If
God sent illness to bring about repentance or if it was caused by
an evil spirit, it was necessary that supernatural rather than natural
means should be used.

The implication that there may be meaning or purpose in illness
beyond the simple physical reality stood in sharp contrast with the
Greek medical tradition where the whole point of medicine was to
treat disease as a natural phenomenon. Indeed, one of Hippocrates'
most famous writings was devoted to demonstrating that epilsepsy
or falling sickness was an ordinary disease which had physical

causes and treatment instead of its being understood as divine possession.[24]

One might speculate that Christian suspicion of medicine not only reflected a profound difference in perspective and world view on the meaning of illness, but also owed something to practical rivalry between Christian and medical healing methods.Clearly, one of the things which commended Christianity to a wider audience was its strong emphasis on effective spiritual healing. Perceived rivals with practical skills to offer would not be popular:

> Christianity came into the world as the religion of healing, as the joyful Gospel of the Redeemer and of the Redemption. It addressed itself to the disinherited, to the sick and afflicted, and promised them healing, a restoration both spiritual and physical . . . The social position of the sick man thus became fundamentally different from what it had been before. He assumed a preferential position which has been his ever since.[25]

The Christian church has continued to fight vigorously for the primacy of its own perspective on disease. Although it moved away from a primary concern about the physical body and bodily healing in order to emphasize the importance of life hereafter in the Middle Ages, this did not lead to much affirmation of medicine.[26] Indeed members of religious communities, who tended to develop skills in physical medicine, were actively discouraged from doing this in the thirteenth century. Laws were passed to forbid the dissection of bodies, a measure which probably had a very negative effect on the development of anatomy and surgery. Further legislation required that physicians should always summon a priest to an ill person so that they could hear a confession which would aid healing if illness was caused by sin and prepare them for the afterlife if their condition was terminal. All these laws were oriented towards keeping the attention of religious, priests, physicians and lay people firmly fixed on the spiritual life to come.[27]

It would be churlish but accurate to point out that control over access and status in the life after death considerably enhanced the status and power of the church on earth. There was no way, within this world view, that church leaders would allow their influence to be eroded by concentration on eliminating physical disease. In any case, many would probably have argued that physical affliction was good for the soul. To put this in proportion, however, it must be remembered that medical methods based on herbalism, crude surgery and humoralism were hardly astonishingly successful. Furthermore, ordinary people were probably entirely pragmatic in their choice of treatment. They would use what was available and, in a situation where most disease was incurable except by spontaneous remission, it was probably a good thing that the church emphasized a better world to come. This gave inevitable illness and discomfort some meaning and purpose.[28]

The point to emphasize is that the church in the mediaeval period had scant respect for medicine and tried to control it in every way possible (the ultimate act of religious control over medicine was when one mediaeval pope had his physician burned for giving him unacceptable advice!) Although the church authorities could not stop people consulting the spiritual and physical healers of their choice, it tried its best to do so.

In England until the end of the seventeenth century or so, physicians, surgeons and midwives were licensed by diocesan bishops.[29] It was only from that time onwards that these occupations began to gain real autonomy from the church. Seventeenth- and eighteenth-century England saw quite an overlap between medical and clerical personnel; it was fairly common for educated people to practise in both spheres.[30] The tradition of clergy having some medical training continued on into the nineteenth century.[31] Qualified physicians were few and far between, so parish clergy had to give what assistance they could to ailing parishioners. But finally clergy were excluded from the realm of medicine (having for the most part previously rejected specifically spiritual or miraculous healing methods) by the formal rise of the medical profession. This was confirmed by the mid-nineteenth-century Medical Registration Act which excluded all but qualified doctors from practising medicine.

If the church and clergy have been driven from the formal practice of medicine, they are always trying to re-assert their influence and control within the sphere of healing and illness. Perhaps the revival of charistmatic healing and the growth of organizations like the Churches' Council for Health and Healing or the Institute of Religion and Medicine can be seen as a protest against exclusion. It is certainly the case that the world of physical medicine never lacks religious critics.

The list of medical practices which the churches have objected to on theological grounds reads like a catalogue of lost causes. Christians have objected to inoculation (unnatural), contraception (defeats the creative purpose of God), anaesthetics, blood transfusions and quarantine measures against epidemic diseases like cholera (all of which were held to be unnatural or frustrations of God's purposes). As recently as the last century and certainly in many previous epidemics, Christians insisted on emphasizing the purpose of God in disease and calling people together for prayer meetings which may have helped to spread disease even while their ostensible purpose of bringing about public repentance was supposed to avert it.[32] In the very recent past, Christians have been very resistant to public health measures aimed at preventing sexually transmitted diseases. Allan Brandt chronicles the way that evangelical Christians in America opposed sex education for children, deplored the giving of contraceptives to troops going off to the First World War, and objected to the free availability of treatment for those who contracted venereal diseases on the grounds that this would encourage immorality.[33]

Lurking behind these views are traditional Christian notions of morality and the ancient but persistent idea that illness has a theological meaning – it is sent to punish, discipline, reform. As long as religion sees itself as actively interpreting the hand of God in particular types of illness and suffering, it seems inevitable that it will clash often and painfully with a humanistic medical tradition which only seeks to understand disease in order to eliminate it.

Perhaps this explains why there seems so little interest amongst medical personnel in contemporary medico-religious dialogue and co-operation.[34] A friend of mine who asked a doctor what Christians could usefully do in the light of the AIDS crisis was told, 'Keep out of the way'. There seems to be a good deal of tension and conflict then between religion and medicine today. This is embodied in the comment quoted. Evidence also comes from some of the attitudes portrayed by charismatic Christian healers. They seem to take a view not dissimilar to the mediaeval papacy, namely that the only good healing is religious or spiritual healing and that the medicine is a second-best alternative with possible demonic associations.

There is certainly continuing scope for fundamental disagreement and misunderstanding. Contemporary medicine, for example, occupies a prominent place in society as a whole. It is highly technical, professionalized, curatively oriented, dismissive of the non-empirical, and very much focussed on centralized medical facilities. It has little time for finding meaning in illness and suffering, preferring to eliminate these things instead.[35] Christianity, on the other hand, is simply one religious option amongst many in a highly secularized society. Its values may seem arbitrary and arcane to many doctors. Generally speaking, it is not technical, it is becoming less professionalized in terms of its ministry, it concentrates on the well-being of people in society and it takes a mysterious realm of the spirit very seriously. At the same time, what it has to offer in practical terms is often not very apparent to medical practitioners who have to meet immediate demands.[36]

Arguably, there is really not very much in common between contemporary Christianity with its rather traditional institutions and attitudes, and modern medicine. Certainly, if they encounter each other in practice they are likely to be as much in conflict as they are to be in agreement. It is tempting to hypothesize that where two world views which have been so much at odds with each other over the centuries seem to be utterly at peace and in harmony, one side must have sold out and become acculturated into the way of thinking of the other. Sadly, the almost total silence between religion and medicine at the moment betokens not tranquillity and agreement but indifference. And it is the once-dominant Christian religion which has ceased to matter, despite its continuing expression of theological views on medical matters ranging from in-vitro fertilization to needles for drug addicts in danger of contracting AIDS.

Where there is any meaningful and significant relationship at all between religion and medicine, there is likely to be real conflict. The history of the relationship between Christianity and medicine is in many ways one of conflicting world views and vying for power rather than one of homogenization and harmony. It is within this horizon that modern medico-religious co-operation and dialogue should be placed.

It should, however, be remembered that if Christians have entered into conflictual relationships with doctors over matters of healing and illness, they have saved most of their criticism, bile and hostility for each other. Here is Bishop Hensley Henson in full and scurrilous polemic against the revival of 'miraculous healing' in the early part of this century:

Christianity stands to lose by its association with miraculous healing. Historically this has been the door through which superstition has found its easiest entrance into the Church. Nor is this to be marvelled at. For miraculous healing is not a Christian phenomenon. It has for Christians no religious significance.[37]

The whole of the book from which that extract comes is an intemperate and intolerant tract aimed firmly at the head of James Moore Hickson and his revivalist friends.[38] Such value as Henson's critique of Hickson has is thoroughly vitiated by his evident contempt and loathing for a different perspective than his own. Similarly vitriolic examples from the opposite perspective are, of course, available.

Politics and Conflict in Everyday Medical Life

It is very difficult to find an area of modern medical life which is not affected in a profound and continuous way by issues of power and conflict. I have already alluded to the *Black Report* on inequalities in health which shows conclusively that poorer people in our society experience more disease and higher mortality than those in higher classes.[39] In a later chapter, I shall be discussing the position of mentally ill people. It seems to be the case that if you come from the lower social classes you have more likelihood of developing mental disorders of one kind or another, that you are less likely to receive the treatment facilities that you need, and that your illness is likely to go on for longer and be more severe. The greater incidence of mental disorder among women than men also seems to point to fundamental social injustice – is it because women are deprived of social control and the self-esteem which it brings that they eventually contract mental disease? This certainly seems a promising explanation when it is recognized that men too seem to suffer from more mental and physical disorders if they become unemployed.[40] In broad terms, it is generally true to say that those who are highest up the scale in terms of class, status and power, suffer less from all kinds of disease, live longer and have access to better health care resources while they are alive. The reverse seems to be the case for people in lower social classes. Although the exact mechanisms whereby this situation comes to prevail are obscure, it can be said with some confidence that inequalities in health reflect inequalities of power and opportunity in society generally. The implication of all this is that illness and healing facilities in our society fairly precisely reflect issues of social and political power and what Marxists would call the 'class struggle'.

Similar issues of conflict, power and inequality are to be found at all levels of the health care system. Now that its very existence is threatened, people tend to idealize the National Health Service and to regard it as having come down from heaven with the willing assent of politicians of all parties in 1948. In fact, the evolution of the Health Service (for it was an evolution) was characterized by severe conflicts right up to the moment of its inauguration. The famous last-minute resistance of the British Medical Association worried about issues like the sale of general practices, dismissal procedures and the possibility of being directed by government, was only the last of a very long string of conflicts at all levels of society and government about the desirability of a state-run universal health care provision system.[41] In the end, the objections of the BMA were crushed by an alliance between the government of the day and the consultants – politics again!

Although there came to be considerable consensus about the merits of the National Health Service for a large number of years (1948 until *c.* 1970) it should be recognized that this has not meant an end to conflicts either within or about that institution. It has been criticized for being a system for rationing scarce medical resources rather than making them widely available, for failing to reduce differential morbidity and mortality in the population (as with many other facilities, it may be that the rich and powerful make best use of the available resources and receive the best standards of care), for providing a type of professionalized, technical and curative medicine which takes patients' sense of their own competence and responsibility for exercising preventive care away from them, and for promoting a rigid, bureaucratic and hierarchical form of centralized health care which is unresponsive to people's own sense of perceived need.[42] These criticisms have come from all parts of the political spectrum.

Since 1970, consensus about the welfare state in general and about the National Health Service in particular has collapsed.[43] The Health Service is once again a political 'football'. Issues of what sort of care people are entitled to, from whom, in what circumstances and with what degree of patient, professional or governmental control and fiscal support have become central. In other words, all public healing provision in this country is made within the context of very serious and far-reaching conflicts between powerful and not so powerful interest groups about what makes for health and what sort of healing should be available.

Conflicts between interest groups with political vested interests and very different perspectives are not confined to the 'macro' level of the National Health Service as a whole. Any observant person can see them in operation in particular health care institutions such as hospitals. Doing research into psychiatric hospitals a few years ago, I was able to identify the following obvious areas of conflict.

1. *Aims*   Most people would probably identify the primary aim of a hospital of any kind as being to ensure that health care resources are made available to ill people so they can recover and, where possible, resume their place in society. Alongside, and sometimes in tension with, this aim are some subsidiary aims, however. These include the need to teach health care professionals, to undertake medical and nursing research, to protect the public from dangerous or undesirable people and to care for people who cannot re-enter society because they are incurable. All of these goals, any one of which may be central to a particular group in the hospital while it is disputed by others, can conflict with each other directly and indirectly in everyday life. They may also conflict with a very important but informal goal of the hospital, namely to run as a smooth bureaucratic organization.[44]

2. *Hierarchical Confusion*   Despite recent management reforms which have attempted to clarify chains of command and responsibility, it is still possible to identify three relatively autonomous hierarchies within most hospitals. These are nursing, medicine and administration.[45] Clearly, it is hoped that these different groups will work closely together at all levels so that a common goal can be identified and striven for. Equally clearly, however, there is much scope for disagreement, misunderstanding and non-cooperation between the different hierarchies.

3. *Power and Status*   There are considerable disparities of relative status and power in hospitals which generally mirror those of society as a whole. Doctors are a tiny minority group within any hospital, yet they have the greatest status and power. They are

highly educated, which in itself carries the implication that they come largely from the highest social classes. The majority of doctors are white men and all patients in hospital are assigned to a doctor who has the power, at least in theory, to direct their treatment exactly as he sees fit. In a real sense, patients actually 'belong' to doctors. Qualified nurses are far more numerous than doctors and have a great deal more to do directly with patients. They tend to come from more middle-class backgrounds and generally have fewer academic qualifications. If the focus of doctors tends to be on curing patients, the task of nurses is actually to care for them while they are in hospital. Most nurses are women. Still further down the hierarchy of status and power are the unqualified nursing staff, who tend to come from working-class backgrounds and who are therefore relatively poorly educated. These workers have little formal power within hospitals, but they work closely with patients and in this capacity they have considerable informal power to affect their lives. Many of these unqualified assistants are women, often from ethnic minorities.[46]

The point of anatomizing the hospital in this way is to show the enormous scope which exists for conflict and misunderstanding to enter into the care and treatment of patients. Powerful doctors may want 'their' patients to be actively treated, while qualified nurses think this is inadvisable and unqualified nursing assistants are simply interested in keeping good order and having a quiet life. The scandals of mistreatment of patients in psychiatric hospitals reported in the 1970s owed much to breakdowns of communication and trust between different groups with different goals, motivations and degrees of power and influence.[47] In the end, and this is the most important thing to note, it is patients who have to bear the cost of this kind of overt and implicit conflict. It is not surprising, then, to find that patients in all types of health care facility often feel confused about what is happening to them. They may rightly suspect that all that is being done does not necessarily reflect a concern for their best interests.

It can be argued that conflict and power issues impinge even on the most personal encounter between an individual doctor and a particular patient in, say, the surgery of a general practice. It has already been noted that doctors tend to come from the highest social classes. This, together with the charismatic authority they derive from their healing work and the role of gate-keeper for scarce medical resources makes them powerful and respected members of the community. Freidson notes that the physician in the consulting room may 'be said to have the manifest status of the expert consultant and the latent status of his prestige in the community'.[48]

Most patients consulting doctors are necessarily from lower social class backgrounds and have very different life experiences and world views from their physicians. They have to negotiate with the doctor an acceptable view of their illness and the treatment appropriate to it. Large communication gaps born of differences in education and experience have to be crossed to do this and, inevitably, the doctor has the upper hand. In the end it is he who can refuse the patient treatment or offer diagnosis and treatment which is not acceptable. In the National Health Service where patients do not pay directly for the service of their physicians and may have little choice about which doctor they are registered with in practice (this is particularly the case in deprived urban areas), a person may be able to do very little to influence the outcome of a medical consultation (perhaps 'confrontation' might be a better word in some circumstances), except not to comply with medical instructions, a form of indirect resistance. In this connection, it has often been noted how many prescriptions are never presented to be made up and how many medicines are thrown away in defiance of medical wisdom.[49]

The purpose of this section has been to show that issues of power and conflict permeate the main secular healing systems of our country at all levels. They directly affect the lives and well-being of all patients and health workers with serious and sometimes adverse consequences. I have not dealt here with the way in which these issues impinge upon religious methods and practitioners of healing, but I have no reason to doubt that empirical research would demonstrate similar effects within the religious sphere. It seems obvious, for example, that religious healers of all kinds wish to appear more powerful than those who come to them for help in order to obtain their clients' confidence and compliance.[50] It seems very probable that religious healing embodies a similar covert concern with control, power, negotiation and conflict, even if these are not words which are often overtly used in discourse about healing.

This concludes my survey of some aspects of power and conflict as they impinge upon healing and illness. My final task in this chapter is to discuss appropriate Christian responses to them.

Towards a Contemporary Christian Response

Illnesses and healing of any kind take place within a specific socio-political context and are inevitably embroiled in issues of power, conflict and control. To many Christians concerned about healing, such a conclusion may seem alien or unacceptable. Even charismatic healers who appear happy to talk of *fighting* the *forces* of evil as they manifest themselves in physical illness and *bind* devils as they exercise *power* healing might be unwilling to look at healing and illness on the wider scale which I have outlined here.

Part of the problem lies in a reluctance on the part of Christians to take the social and political implications of healing seriously. They want to see these phenomena in individualistic terms. In particular, they want to see healing as a straightforward and unambivalent form of individual benevolence. The fact that such an attitude prevents the necessity for asking hard questions about the motives and effects of healers, as well as allowing them not to have to raise questions about the wider social order, is an additional advantage here. But if my critique has any validity at all, it seems important to draw out its practical implications for contemporary Christian response to illness and healing.

The first point to make here is that words like power and conflict should not necessarily be taken in a pejorative or negative sense. The whole of life is full of conflicts and power relationships from the interactions between parents and children through to those of governments and sovreign states. They are necessary, often creative and, in any case, inevitable. For some reason, Western Christians have come to fight shy of conflict. For them, harmony, reconciliation and wholeness are represented by a world without conflict. Perhaps this anxiety accounts in part for the relative lifelessness of many churches. If so, it could be that a proper recognition of the importance and potential of power and conflict would be reviving. Power and conflict should not be seen as dubious and immoral in themselves. They need to be rehabilitated and directly addressed in the life of the churches in general and in perspectives on healing and illness in particular. Ignoring these dimensions does not make them go away, it just means that they are unregarded and unassessed. This maximizes their harmful potential.

A corollary of this is that Christians should be prepared to examine far more carefully elements of conflict and power as they affect healing and illness. The knowledge of these factors should precede uncritical acclamation of particular ways of healing. It should also act as a question mark against precipitate action. A basic principle in medicine is to do the sick no harm. By paying attention to which is being 'said' by particular forms of illness and healing and to the values and power relations which are being affirmed, as well as those which are being denied, Christians stand some chance of avoiding unfortunate associations with healing practices which are less than desirable. This is not to say that all types of healing are necessarily suspect or that all illnesses are intimately bound up with social control or protest against it. It is just to sound a warning that these things *may* be involved in any particular situation and it is important to be aware of them if they are. Close attention to the implications of healing methods may lead Christians into having to make difficult choices between methods. So be it; it is better to make choices than to take things at their face value and find that they are ultimately harmful.

The points made so far can be 'grounded' in a concrete example. It is well known that many working class women suffer disproportionately from the mental disorder known as depression.[51] Research suggests that these women regard this 'disease' like other diseases as coming from outside themselves so they have no control over it.[52] If they go to doctors they are likely to have this view reinforced by the fact that medical practitioners use the language of disease and tend to prescribe organic treatments such as anti-depressant drugs. If such women consulted some kinds of Christian healers, they might not use the language of disease to describe the disorder. They might, however, be quite likely to use prayer or healing methods such as laying on of hands. These might suggest equally effectively to the women that somehow some force from outside was what was needed to cure them.

Both medically-prescribed drugs and spiritual healing methods might confirm to the women that they were the passive victims of disease or disorder and that they themselves could do nothing about it. This kind of affirmation would stand in stark contrast to the views and methods which might be advanced by some sociologists and psychologists. The former would suggest that women suffer disproportionately from depression because they are relatively impotent in contemporary society and so suffer from a lack of self-esteem and hopelessness.[53] Healing, on this model, would demand that women were more centrally involved in controlling their own destinies, perhaps by achieving in the outside world rather than being confined to the domestic sphere where their confidence is eroded. One of the things which might facilitate this could be a greater range of choices about employment opportunities. This perspective is complemented by that of those psychologists who suggest that the way out of the prison of depression does not lie so much in the passive receipt of drugs, but in making active choices about life, which enhance a sense of autonomy and self-esteem. Once again, equal job opportunities for women outside the home, or at least giving women the chance to *choose* whether or not to take up such opportunities, might represent a positive method of healing.[54]

The view of what it is to be human, healthy and whole embodied in the differing methods of healing implicitly represented on the one side by the medical and spiritual perspectives, and on the other by those of sociology and psychology is a very different one. Each perspective carries substantial implications for the social and political position of women in society. The one affirms passivity and the social order which forces women to become depressed. The other points strongly towards an increase in personal autonomy and, by implication, to fundamental social change which encourages greater equality between the sexes. Healing methods, therefore, have substantial social and political ramifications which must be recognized and addressed if true healing is to occur.

This brings me to two theological comments. In the light of the foregoing discussion, there would seem to be much to be said for seeing an important part of healing in terms of revealing.[55] Many healing methods, both religious and secular, may cure people in the sense that they remove symptoms and allow a return to 'normal' functioning in society. The question is, is this enough? Surely there should be an element of healing which pays attention to actually helping a person see what sort of situation he or she is in. This enables a person actually to choose how to tackle it, rather than opting for a curative method which may be damaging in its side-effects (and I suggest that methods which strongly encourage people to regard themselves as entirely passive in regard to their own illnesses should be seen as having damaging side-effects). It is true, of course, that there may be circumstances in which a person can do nothing about their own situation and must be passive while treatment is administered to them by others. Even in these circumstances, though, it is possible to help a person to gain a perspective on things which may help them to have a sense of control, however slight.

I am not suggesting that only methods which enhance individual autonomy and control are valid in healing. I do, however, want to advocate a more active understanding in regard to healing than has been popular in religious circles hitherto. Discerning the truth of one's own situation, or that of one's group, allows real choice about healing methods and attitudes to illness. This in itself may be therapeutic. It certainly demands more active human participation at more levels than simply taking tablets or having hands laid upon oneself. To return to the example of depressed women; perhaps healing for them would really begin once they began to understand why they were depressed and what they needed to do to prevent this occurring.

The administration of spiritual or medical nostrums which take away symptoms while leaving fundamental causes unchanged might be regarded as no more than 'cheap healing' analogous to Bonhoeffer's 'cheap grace'. The point can be further illuminated by reference to Freud. He suggested that undertaking psychoanalysis did not cure people in the first instance, but rather gave them self-knowledge which potentially enhanced their life and choices. In the same way, I am suggesting here that knowledge and discernment in regard to illness, its context, causes and treatment should be the fundamental component of religious healing. In any case, it should always accompany attempts to cure. Perhaps, then, the Christian response to illness and its first step towards healing should be seen in terms of active revelation and discernment of what is going on, rather than in terms of direct action.

If healing should be seen in the first instance in terms of revelation, a complementary viewpoint would be to regard faith primarily in terms of human action. The idea that faith is closely related to healing has been present in the Christian healing tradition since the time of Jesus' own ministry. Nearly all writers on healing regard faith as essential. There is, however, considerable debate on the nature of the faith which is needed for healing to take place. Some suggest that the person needing healing must have faith, others that it is necessary for those who pray for them to have faith.[56] A factor which unites these writers is the underlying notion that faith means trust in God. In practice, this again seems to promote a rather passive view of healing which should perhaps be corrected. Such correction is provided by modern political theologians who argue that faith is not a matter of putting trust in God and then waiting patiently to see what happens. Instead, it is active involvement to appropriating salvation for oneself and others.

This point is powerfully made by the South African theologian, Albert Nolan in his book *Jesus Before Christianity*. Nolan sees the situation of the people amongst whom Jesus worked as being one of fatalism and despair. Jesus' ministry of healing was important not so much because of the signs and wonders in themselves, but because they witnessed to the possibility of the triumph of good over evil. This was a counter blast to fatalism. It enabled people to have hope in their own destiny and struggle against the things which oppressed them. Nolan writes:

> Faith is a good and a true conviction. It is the conviction that something can and will happen because it is good and because it is true that goodness can and will triumph over evil. . . . The power of faith is the power of goodness and truth, which is the power of God.[57]

In the light of this kind of perspective it could be said that faith healing in our own time consists not so much of people feeling that their situation has been improved by the direct and mighty acts of God to relieve their sickness, but in people gaining the confidence and hope which allows them to address the social and political structures which oppress them and cause illness. Faith is not primarily passive waiting upon God. It is the active struggle for healing and wholeness amidst the socio-political complexities, ambiguities and conflicts of an industrialized society which makes many people sick and deprives them of real hope in the future.[58] With our major secular health care institutions under threat, there has never been a more important time for faithful Christian healing of a kind which is prepared to act within situations of conflict.

Chapter Five

Responding to Mental Illness

In the last two chapters of this work, I want to look more closely at two particular kinds of disease and religious responses to them, both actual and potential. I hope that this will exemplify and make more concrete some of the points made in general and abstract ways in previous chapters and that it will show more clearly the practical significance of the whole of my critique. The next chapter deals with the very latest pandemic to confront the human race, AIDS. In this chapter, however, I consider one of the oldest and most prevalent disorders on the face of the earth – mental illness.

Like the poor, mentally ill people and mental disorder seem to be with us always. Whether or not you choose to see some of Jesus' healing miracles, particularly the exorcisms, as instances of mental disorder being cured, there can be no doubt that phenomena which correspond in terms of personal and social disruption to what we now call mental illness have been universal in all human societies and cultures:

> Every society recognizes certain extreme forms of aberrant behavior as mental derangement or insanity. In other words, along the range of human behavior, from that which a society considers normal to that which it regards as abnormal, there is some point or section at which a social judgement is made and an individual comes to be regarded as mad.[1]

In many ways, there is no more important disorder for Christians to study and respond to than mental illness. It is estimated, probably conservatively, that some two hundred and fifty million of the world's population suffer from severe mental illness. In the

UK no less than 11% of all men and 17% of all women are ill enough to be hospitalized in a psychiatric facility during the course of their lives, 60% of National Health Service hospital beds are devoted to mental illness patients, and one million people receive psychiatric care of some sort each year.[2] It is a measure of the extent to which we can ignore the unpalatable or unpleasant that mental illness is thought to be only a problem for a minority of the population. In fact, many people are affected by it personally and through their relations much of the time, certainly far more than those who are and will be affected by AIDS in the near future. The continuing epidemic of mental illnesses of various kinds is reduced in its appalling significance by its sheer omniprevalence and unwanted familiarity. The fact that it is relatively unregarded, by Christians as much as by the general population, does not mean it is insignificant. Mental illness will continue to present an enormous, perpetual but hidden challenge to all healing systems for the foreseeable future.[3]

Having acknowledged the importance of mental disorder as a field for theoretical study and practical response, it must also be said it is a highly complex and variegated one. Mental illness is not a single entity. It can be divided into neuroses, psychoses, obsessional disorders and anxiety states.[4] Although therapeutic developments have occurred over the centuries, their achievements have been partial, as has real knowledge of mental disease. In fact, the whole notion of seeing mental disorder as primarily disease or illness is itself problematic as we shall see; psychiatry represents one of the few areas of medical life and knowledge where there is great pluralism of perspectives on fundamental issues and this leads in turn to very different clinical and helping responses. All this is by way of warning the reader that the issues I cover and the accounts that I will give of them must perforce be very generalized. My purpose, as in the rest of the book, is to open up this area for attention and discussion, not to provide a definitive textbook.

I shall now proceed with a brief account of the history of perceptions of mental disorder and its treatment in which particular attention will be paid to responses and perspectives from Christianity and Christian theology. A survey of modern perspectives on mental disorder follows in which the social and political context of mental illness and its treatment will be emphasized. This forms a prelude to suggesting some possible practical and theological religious responses to mental disorder today.

Historical Perspectives and Background

From the earliest times, there has never been one single way of understanding the sorts of abnormal behaviour which might today be identified as mental illness. Ancient societies, like contemporary traditional societies, recognized the possibility of supernatural possession by good or evil spirits. Possession by a good spirit led to the attribution of the role of prophet or to the recognition of divine favour, while invasion by an evil spirit required some form of exorcism. There was considerable ambivalence here; consider the case of Saul in the Old Testament who appears to have experienced possession by both kinds of spirit at various points in his life. This ambivalence in interpreting the nature of a divine or evil spirit was complicated by the fact that there was also a clear tradition that madness was a physical illness, a natural misfortune which could be accounted for and cured by natural means. The ancient Greek medical tradition broadly adhered to this position and used the techniques of humoral medicine to treat the insane, but it seems likely that all traditional societies used such physical remedies as were available to treat disorders which were not perceived to have a supernatural cause.[5]

Ambiguity about the nature of mental disorder, about divine versus natural causation and about the positive or negative character of supernatural possession has continued to complicate perceptions and responses to mental disorder until the very recent past.[6] But there can be no doubt that early Christianity gave an enormous boost to the supernaturalist view, and particularly to the idea that mental abnormality was caused by evil spirits or demons. Screech asserts that 'Madness and Christianity go hand in hand.'[7] In a paper on 'Good madness in Christendom', he goes on to develop the notion that from its earliest beginnings almost to the present day Christian other-worldliness has been bound up with diabolical and organic madness. The ministry of Jesus is important in this connection, for Jesus is portrayed as divinely possessed by a good spirit as well as being involved in a war against disorderly evil spirits. Paul talks of Christianity as a divine madness whereby people are drawn out of the conventionalities of this world to join in the purpose of God.[8] Clearly his own personal experience is punctuated by the sorts of ecstacy which would be seen as good madness by pagans as well as Christians.

These themes are later developed by Renaissance thinkers like Erasmus who again suggest that the manias and ecstasies of the madman can reveal something of the divine by virtue of inducing detachment from the realities of the fallen unspiritual material world.[9] But if madness could be good, it could also be demonic and bad. It is this latter tradition which seems to have dominated the early church whose legacy to Christian responses to mentally abnormal behaviour seems to have been the demonization of the mentally disordered. Fear and loathing of possession united the early church against the Kingdom of Satan which warred against the Kingdom of God; Christianity provided the remedy for fear (exorcism), but only after it had heightened that fear in the first place.[10]

The curiously contradictory attitudes of seeing madness sometimes as blessedness, sometimes as demonically inspired and sometimes as natural misfortune probably continued into the Dark Ages and mediaeval period.[11] In his survey of mental disorder in earlier Britain, Basil Clarke emphasizes the fact that the supernatural explanations and remedies were probably not as prominent as those of natural causation and cure. They were, however, always regarded as possible understandings and methods which could revive in particular circumstances, as they still do. Thus Screech claims,

> the Renaissance doctor, faced with mad-seeming behaviour or with special powers in apparently mad people, had to step with care. He might be dealing with a purely natural illness . . . ; he might be dealing with evil spirits who require exorcising. Or . . . he might be dealing, not with evil or illness at all, but with the privileged mania of a saint.[12]

At the local everyday level in England, it should be noted that not much was really done to care for mad people. Bethlem Hospital in London was a tiny monastic initiative to care for a few of the mentally disordered from the thirteenth century onwards. In general, though, mentally ill people wandered where they wished. They were the responsibility of their families, if of anyone.[13] Rosen describes the attitude of people in ancient Greece and Rome to the insane as being one where fear and contempt were mingled to a lesser extent with an element of compassion.[14] Despite the putative blessedness and privilege of these people within the Christian tradition, one wonders whether they actually received the honour and provision which their position notionally allowed them.

The mists which shroud the attitudes and treatments surrounding mentally ill people in Western society begin to clear in terms of modern historical scholarship at around the turn of the seventeenth century. In his fascinating study of the cleric, physician and astrologer Richard Napier (1549–1634), Rector of Great Linford in Buckinghamshire, Michael MacDonald situates mental disorder at a nexus between the natural and supernatural.[15]

The social and the moral, the natural and the supernatural, the normal and the abnormal were all closely related and could influence each other. Science, medicine and religion could not be absolutely distinguished. Thus it was possible to ascribe the causes of mental disorder to emotional upset, to natural causes or to supernatural sources. In so far as the whole of life was bound together, it was possible to see that the Devil could use natural human weakness to accomplish his evil purposes. The inner life of a person could be regarded as a moral allegory whereby madness could be equated with sin, sanity with grace, despair with apostasy and anxiety with spiritual doubt. Religious language could provide a vocabulary for mental anguish, while people were healed by having their bodies and minds restored to harmony within the unity of the divinely-ordained natural order.[16] Napier's healing methods ranged from exorcism and the making of amulets and charms through to prayer and the prescription of natural remedies. For him, there was no significant difference between the magical, the medical and the spiritual.

Napier stood at the threshold of the modern world where medical psychology or natural understandings and treatments have come to dominate the realm of mental disorder, and the supernatural has become highly suspect. Nonetheless, in his study of madness in the seventeenth and eighteenth centuries Roy Porter is able to assert the continuing significance of the religious and metaphysical dimensions of mental disorder:

During the seventeenth and eighteenth centuries madness was an extremely broad cultural category with many manifestations and meanings. Madness could be seen as medical, or moral, or religious, or indeed, Satanic. It could be sited in the mind or the soul, in the brain or the body. It could be good or bad . . . And the language of madness served not only to diagnose desperately disturbed individuals but also more metaphorically, to express wider moral and political values.[17]

Despite great pluralism in viewpoint as to the causes and treatments of mental disorder, particularly at a popular level, (these included moral and character defects, emotional difficulties, organic and hereditary factors and even some kinds of religious experience like Methodism and enthusiasm), rationalism and physical viewpoints came to decisive domination over spiritual and religious views of madness: 'There was . . . a deep-seated disposition to view abnormalities as body-based.'[18] This perspective minimized personal responsibility, guilt and shame. However, it also ensured that no longer would madness be seen as having any positive or spiritual value. Furthermore, it helped to ensure the segregation and derogation of the insane whose disorders were now seen as worthless and whose voice was no longer worth attending to from the point of view of physicians and other therapists:

> earlier traditions had treated the voices of the mad as important; all too often dangerous (as with demonic possession); perhaps revelatory, as with the mad prophet or poet. Those became undercut.[19]

The eighteenth century, then, saw the truimph of essentially physical views of mental disorder and its treatment, though it has to be said that this did not mean great advances in medical treatment. Basically, traditional humoral methods, e.g. purging and blood letting, were the only medical treatments available. An important new development, however, was that of moral management. This was based on fundamentally mentalist theory which suggested that the way to cure the insane was by intensive personal contact. It allowed a therapist to gain control over the disordered mind of his patient and thus to change the false conceptions of reality suffered by the patient. Therapy became a matter of correcting mental misapprehension and error. At first this was to be undertaken only with individuals, but moral management found its fullest expression in the asylum regimes of the nineteenth century.[20]

Here Christians play a more overtly significant part again, for it was William Tuke, a Quaker layman whose experiment in communal moral management at The Retreat in York was to set the tone for all other asylums in the country. Asylums were not new when Tuke began The Retreat in 1792. Small asylums had begun in the middle of the eighteenth century (they were complemented by private madhouses which might only accommodate one or two lunatics) but these chiefly used medical and mechanical restraint methods to treat patients.[21] The difference between them and The Retreat was that Tuke was determined to treat his patients with humanity and firmness, without physical restraint.[22] At its simplest, Tuke's underlying philosophy was that if you treat people as people, recognizing the God-given humanity within them, they are more likely to become well again and behave like people.

The Retreat became the model for asylums and, in the nineteenth century, asylums became the main way of treating mentally disordered people. By the middle of the century legislation had been passed which required all civic authorities to provide asylum care for lunatics within their administration. As new asylums were built, they filled to bursting point with the insane. All major towns and cities sprouted asylums on their edges; unfortunately, highly personalized moral treatment or management became an impossibility in these circumstances and the asylums quickly became warehouses for the chronically mentally disordered.[23] Control within the asylum quickly passed to medical professionals.[24] Their authority to identify and manage madness on the model of any other disease was finally enshrined in pre-war legislation in this century which re-named lunacy as mental illness and lunatic asylums as mental hospitals.

The dominance of medical perspectives on mental disorder continues to the present day in this country but the asylum is now in decline. Since 1959, it has been government policy to transfer mentally ill people back into the community from whence they were extruded over a century ago.[25]

I want to go on shortly to discuss the position of mentally ill people in contemporary society and the implications of various kinds of treatment used with them, but first there are some threads which should be drawn out of the historical account above.

One aspect to be underlined is the sheer diversity of ways of looking at and treating mental disorder over the centuries. Related to this is the importance of the religious and supernatural significance attached to mental disorder through much of human history, and, conversely, the almost complete withdrawal of religious interest in and concern about mental disorder during the eighteenth century. Since that time, Christian involvement in this area of human experience has been limited to occasional bursts of enthusiasm for different types of medical or moral treatment. The evangelical Earl of Shaftesbury, for example, was a great proponent of asylum care in the last century. In our own time, some organizations which provide care or therapy for mentally ill people, e.g., the Richmond Fellowship, have some basis in humanistic Christian commitment.

A third point which should be made is that perspectives on, and treatments of, mental disorder have not progressed smoothly from darkness into light so that now mentally ill people are being treated better than at any other time in their history. Mental disorder has always been an enigma to the human race. The different viewpoints and treatment methods surveyed above represent fashions in thinking which may have only approximated to the real nature of mental disorder (if it is even remotely possible to talk of a 'real' nature for mental disorder rather than of competing interpretations), much less the actual needs of mentally ill people. The practical consequence of this is that mentally disordered people have all too often had to suffer cruelties and indignities at the hands of their ideologically motivated helpers; lunatics in the eighteenth century were forcibly restrained and beaten because they were regarded as lacking reason like the beasts, and therefore were to be treated as beasts. At a less spectacularly horrific level, lunatics were herded into asylums for years after it became perfectly clear that the therapeutic potential of those institutions was minimal. The reason was that no one could think of a better way of dealing with them in nineteenth- and early-twentieth-century society.

Finally, it should be noted that the treatment of mentally disordered people is shaped by the values, social structures and beliefs of wider society and to some extent reflects social change and conflict. Thus, the decline of formal religion contributed to the de-supernaturalization of mental disorder in the eighteenth century. In the following century, the exclusion of lunatics from urban society into special separate asylums was partly due to the restructuring of the Poor Law which ended payments to needy people outside institutions like workhouses in order to encourage potential workers to compete in the labour market. The impotent poor were enclosed at this time and those who were identified as ill were put into asylums where they would not have to work but where life was unpleasant enough to deter people from feigning mental disorder.[26] The 'medicalization' of mental disorder whereby it came to be regarded as a disease like other illnesses reflects the energy that medical professionals put in to trying to obtain dominance in the asylums.[27]

Perhaps the most important thing to learn from the history of attitudes to and treatments of mental disorder is that the concept of altruistic, harmless progress is far more ambivalent and much more of a myth in regard to mental disorder than to other areas of social life. Many of the concepts and treatments which have been perpetrated on mentally disordered people down the centuries may have done as much harm as they have done good. The ambiguities of 'good' and 'bad' madness are reflected in those of 'good' and 'bad' treatment.[28]

Models of Mental Disorder

The twentieth century has seen no diminution of the range of perspectives and models used to understand and treat mental disorder, even if explanations are now couched in apparently more earthly and less supernatural terms than they once were. A comprehensive survey of these perspectives would be interesting in its own right. It would, however, be over-lengthy and somewhat esoteric for present purposes. What I propose to do here, therefore, is to give a very brief account of some of the more common ways of looking at and treating mental disorder adding some evaluation of their respective merits, disadvantages and implications.

I shall pay particular attention to the social and political implications of each perspective. This is preliminary to arguing that a strong case can be made for seeing mental illness and mentally ill people primarily in social and political terms and for modulating Christian healing responses in that direction. The reason for advocating this viewpoint is that religious people have become trapped so firmly into seeing mental illness simply as an individual misfortune requiring some kind of individual cure. I would not want in any way to deny the reality of individual suffering (who else ultimately can suffer other than the individual?), nor would I want to advocate forsaking the search for effective healing methods for use with suffering individuals. However, I do want to suggest very forcibly that some of the factors which cause people to become ill, keep them ill, and substantially add to their general state of misery, are related to structural factors which therefore demand a structural healing response. So to the survey of contemporary 'models' of mental disorder.[29]

1. The Medical Model   This is by far the most universal and influential way of looking at and treating mental disorder in Britain today. Broadly speaking, the medical or disease model 'regards mental malfunction as a consequence of physical and chemical changes primarily in the brain but sometimes in other parts of the body'.[30] The implication of this assertion is that treatment of mental illness should be conducted primarily along organic lines.[31] So psychiatrists, who, in this country, are always fully qualified medical practitioners, treat mental disorder in the same way as they would treat any other kind of disease. They use physical methods such as drugs, psychosurgery or Electro-convulsive Therapy (ECT). Of these methods, the administration of drugs is the most common. Psychosurgery is only infrequently used these days.

In an age where we have become accustomed to thinking of illness in fundamentally organic terms, it probably seems little more than common sense that mental disorder should also be seen in this light. Although few people would want to deny that there is an organic element in most mental disorders (syphilitic paralysis and senile dementia would appear *prima facie* to have organic causes even if their precise mechanisms are imperfectly understood), it has to be said that psychiatry has been conspicuously unsuccessful in identifying the physical and pathological basis for many mental disorders. The use of medical diagnostic techniques and terminology is justified by defenders of the model by reference to their pragmatic utility and heuristic potential. The argument runs that, whether or not there are discrete mental illnesses like physical illnesses, thinking of mental disorders as illnesses allows effective treatment, prognosis and research. Even if we do not know exactly what we are treating, or why particular drugs have a beneficial effect, the main thing is that these treatments appear to work:

the biologically inclined psychiatrist takes some satisfaction in the fact that the list of conditions in which psychological disturbances appear to be symptomatic of underlying physical pathology continues to expand.[32]

Despite its 'scientific' outer clothing, the disease model of mental disorder rests on probabilities rather than certainties. At the present time, it offers symptom control and relief rather than cure for mental illness. Symptom relief is not to be despised in mental disorder. It is only because people's more florid symptoms have been controlled by physical treatments, notably by the major tranquillizers which became widely available in the 1950s, that so many people are able to live relatively normal lives in hospitals and in the community and that overt violence has ceased to be so closely associated with mental illness.

Insofar as physical treatments have allowed mentally ill people to live more 'normal' lives, the medical model may be regarded as having enhanced their freedom. But there are other implications of this model which may be deemed more socio-politically ambivalent. First, the patient is rendered relatively passive and impotent in the treatment of his own disorder. Conversely, the psychiatrist has great power, not only over the patient whose illness he alone can treat, but also over other helping personnel who cannot prescribe physical treatments though they may have to administer them.[33] Medical treatments are relatively cheap in terms of staff time (though drugs, for example, provide enormous profits for the companies who make them), and this may be an attraction to a government seeking economic ways to control mental disorder on behalf of a society which may be largely indifferent to the long-term interests of the mentally ill.[34] It is not for nothing that the administration of pharmacological agents to patients has sometimes been characterized as 'the liquid cosh'.

Substantive issues of power and control therefore surround the use of the medical model in treating mental disorder. As I noted in a previous chapter, seeing disorders as illnesses allows for their control on an individualistic basis deprives them of their value as protests as well as disguising the importance of wider social and political factors in their causation and cure.[35] The individual is conformed and controlled rather than society being reformed.[36]

2. *The Behavioural Model* In recent years the dominance of the medical model has received a substantial challenge from the essentially behaviourist psychology which underlies much clinical psychology. The very simple principle which informs behaviourism is that all behaviour is learnt and so it can be unlearned or changed through providing a system of rewards and punishments (sanctions) which reinforce desirable behaviour while extinguishing unwanted and anti-social practices. It is maintained that much of the symptomatology which manifests itself in mental disorder can be changed using a regime of sanctions. If outward ways of acting are changed then inner attitudes and social relationships can be changed too.[37] Behaviourist methods are particularly effective, it is maintained, with disorders such as phobic and anxiety states. They can also be used with hospitalized patients with chronic schizophrenia and depression to increase their social competence and reduce their anti-social traits. So, for example, the use of token economies (giving rewards and privileges for desired behaviour) on a hospital ward can counter some of the worst effects of disease and institutionalization.

There are strong similarities between the principles underlying behaviour therapy and the practice of milieu and administrative therapeutic regimes and therapeutic communities.[38] Although practitioners of these latter modes of treatment would not necessarily want to see their descent as being from behaviourism (therapeutic communities, for example, have been more influenced by psychotherapeutic ideas), the basic principle on which they work is that of using group and structural engineering of the therapeutic environment to effect desired change in patients who can then be rehabilitated into society.

Behavioural and group therapies have several advantages over physical treatments. They appear to have a good deal of success with some conditions. They are not physically invasive and therefore they do not provide some of the unpleasant side-effects of psychotropic drug treatments. In social and political terms, they pay more attention to what the patient wants and require the patient's active co-operation if they are to work. Doctors are not necessarily dominant in the administration of these therapies, so control is more widely dissipated. Because they demand more staff time than the prescription of drugs, it may be that these kinds of treatments are more expensive; perhaps this goes some way to explaining the decline of such work within a financially constrained National Health Service. But it must also be noted that if these methods can give patients a greater part in their own treatment and destiny, they can also be oppressive in certain circumstances. Therapeutic communities can simply be places where considerable group pressure is exerted on individuals to change:

> We need . . . have no qualms of guilt about saying that our therapeutic community is going to teach its members certain kinds of behaviour and discourage undesirable behaviour.[39]

Behavioural methods are reasonably egalitarian and enhance ·patients' sense of themselves when practised on a one-to-one basis. (Even here, though, it must be borne in mind that differences of class, status and power may conspire to make the relationship and influence of therapist and patient very unequal.) When implemented with a group of patients, however, they may be very oppressive indeed:

> In order to set up a system of rewards, it is often necessary to deprive patients of other methods of whatever is used as a reward. Hence, although staff may see patients as working for a system of rewards, the patients themselves may feel that they are working to escape from a punishment they have done nothing to deserve . . . Furthermore, the system can never be any better than those administering it, and the power to give rewards can always be misused to persuade patients to do things which are patently for the good of staff members but not so obviously for the patient's good.[40]

While being aware of the negative side of behavioural and administrative regimes, it should not be forgotton that such methods are used outwith psychiatry, e.g., in education and counselling without much controversy.[41]

3. The Psychodynamic Model Psychodynamic models of mental disorder presuppose that such disorder is the product of conflicting emotions deep within the patients personality. Psychotherapies use words and personal and professional relationships to effect alleviation of patients' difficulties.[42] These relationships can be on a one-to-one basis as in the classic psychoanalysis of Freud and his followers who spend regular hours simply listening to one person, or they can be fostered in a group.[43] In the National Health Service it is more common to find group psychotherapy occurring, for the simple reason that individual therapy is obviously very expensive in terms of staff time. But it must be recognized that psychotherapy is not a popular mode of treatment in British psychiatry. This is partly because of its lengthiness and therefore its expense. It also has to do with the fact that it is widely held that as a method it simply does not work effectively with mentally ill people. It is more an indulgence which can be paid for by the mildly neurotic affluent on a private basis rather than a treatment which should be available to all at public expense.

Significantly, it is individual psychotherapy which gives the mentally ill person most time with a skilled professional and therefore maximizes his personal autonomy and freedom to express himself. The therapist is completely dependent on the patient to effect his own cure, he can administer no drug. Although it must be true that psychotherapists can influence their patients significantly in different directions, particularly if they are perceived to be superior in knowledge, wisdom or status, in general psychotherapy implies an equality of relationship which is unusual in the treatment of mental disorder.[44] It is a pity, therefore, that its results are so equivocal and that it is so little available to ordinary people.[45]

4. Custodialism   Custodialism is not an 'official' system of thought and therapy in relation to mental disorder. It is one which has been particularly operative in psychiatric institutions in the absence of other treatment ideologies, funds, staff and morale. The aggregate of miscellaneous views and practices which comprise the 'ideal type' of custodialism has been characterized thus:

> The model of the custodial orientation is the traditional prison and the 'chronic' mental hospital which provide a highly controlled setting concerned mainly with the detention and safekeeping of its inmates. Patients are conceived in stereotyped terms as categorically different from 'normal' people, as totally irrational, insensitive to others, unpredictable and dangerous. Mental illness is attributed primarily to poor heredity, organic lesion and the like. In consequence, the staff cannot expect to understand the patients, to engage in meaningful relationships

with them, nor in most cases to do them any good. Custodialism is saturated with pessimism, impersonalness, and watchful distrust. The custodial conception of the hospital is autocratic, involving as it does a rigid status hierarchy, a unilateral downward flow of power, and a minimizing of communication within and across status lines.[46]

Of all perspectives outlined here this is clearly the most oppressive. Custodialism leads to the institutionalization and demoralization of patients and staff alike.[47] It has no potential for curing people or enhancing their individuality and autonomy. Although it seems eminently undesirable, unfortunately even today elements of custodialism are not uncommon in institutions which are for mentally ill people from psychiatric hospitals through to community care hostels. Custodialism flourishes where resources are scarce, staff are poor and morale is low. It is a cheap option for disposing of groups of people whose social and personal needs are not given a high financial priority by society.[48]

5. Community Care   Partly as a reaction to the negative custodialism of the old asylums, a new way of treating and disposing of the mentally ill has been introduced to Britain in the last thirty years–community care. The underlying assumption of community care is that mentally ill people are likely to be better off living outside large institutions in the community where their needs can be met by a variety of small scale psychiatric and social service provisions, e.g. day-centres, hostels, psychiatric wards in District General Hospitals.[49]

On the face of it, caring for people in the community seems a liberal and humane development. It would appear to give mentally ill people maximum freedom, autonomy and normality in their lives over against the regimentation from which they suffered in the large old asylum hospitals. In practice, the policy seems far more equivocal, however. Little research was done before the policy was implemented to see in what way community care affected patients' recovery from mental illness. Experience in America suggests that patients may even be worse off:

> We have learned what we should have known but missed in our enthusiasm for change. Community life is no panacea unless the patient's suffering is alleviated and social functioning improved.

We have learned that community life, without adequate services and supports could be as dehumanizing and debilitating as the poor mental hospital. We have learned that if the patient is sufficiently disturbed and disoriented . . . residence in the home or community can cause innumerable difficulties for family and others and may result in a general outcome inferior to good institutional care.[50]

Failure to provide good facilities in the community, to co-ordinate community responses, and to educate the general public about mental illness so it welcomes mentally ill people rather than rejecting them leads one to suspect that community care might simply be a euphemism for community neglect. From the government's point of view, it is a cheap way of dealing with mentally ill people who can be maintained in a kind of twilight world of night shelters, sub-standard hostels, isolated housing in the ghetto areas of towns and cities and even on the long-stay wards of the streets themselves at much less expense than in hospital accommodation.[51] Mentally ill people receiving community care are certainly free from many restraints, but they do not seem to have positive freedom to participate fully in main social structures. They may experience greater deprivation, inequality and injustice than they did in the old psychiatric hospitals. It is reprehensible that the long-term effects of community care on mentally ill people have not been assessed before this policy has been implemented as the norm for care provision. One cannot imagine a new drug not receiving clinical trials, but the policy of community care has been implemented without any research into its beneficence or harmful effects.[52] Political and financial expediency dressed up as humanitarian concern has carried the day.

To the politician, 'community care' is a useful piece of rhetoric; to the sociologist, it is a stick to beat institutional care with; to the civil servant, it is a cheap alternative to institutional care which can be passed to the local authorities for action – or inaction; to the visionary, it is a dream of a new society in which people really do care; to the social services departments, it is a nightmare of heightened public expectations and inadequate resources to meet them. We are only just beginning to find out what it means to the old, the chronic sick and the handicapped.[53]

I shall say a bit more about community care in the last part of the chapter but now I want to consider briefly two final models for looking at and treating mental disorder in contemporary society.

6. *Social Deviance*   The idea that illness is essentially a form of social deviance, or negatively sanctioned behaviour was raised in chapter 2 above. The nub of the idea lying behind this model is that all societies have social norms and values and that those who do not conform to these are deviants. In this sense, deviance is in the eye of the beholder; it all depends on what the norms are as to whether you are regarded as a deviant. It is for this reason that deviance theory can be regarded as societal reaction theory; it may tell you more about the norms a society holds than about any particular kind of behaviour in itself.

Deviance theory specifically in relation to mental disorder has been developed into labelling theory. Sociologists like Scheff suggest that mental illness is a name given to anti-social behaviour which is inexplicable on any other ground, e.g., criminal intent. It is a residual category.[54] Once a person is labelled as mentally ill, her behaviour may be reinforced by society and psychiatric institutions which force her to develop a complete and stereotypical role as a mentally ill person (this is known as secondary deviance). If that person then refuses to play this stereotypical role their behaviour is sanctioned once again by the conferment of stigma. Thus it becomes impossible for people to return to an ordinary role in society, they remain perpetually 'ex-mental patients'. According to the strict application of deviance theory to mental disorder there is no treatment or cure for mental illness other than getting a person to conform to social norms or getting society to change those norms.[55]

At first sight this way of looking at mental disorder may seem remote from everyday life and practical concerns, but in fact it highlights some very important factors which are of enormous practical concern. First, it sensitizes us to the fact that there are social and value elements in identifying mental illness; what counts as mental disorder in the Soviet Union would be regarded as political dissent in this country. Secondly, this perspective goes a long way towards explaining why mentally ill people are feared and ignored; the conferring of stigma means that we surround mentally ill people with a negative aura in order to discourage people from behaving in socially deviant ways.[56] It also explains to some extent why people with mental disorders have difficulty in being received back into society; in a perverse and inadvertent way they learn and are encouraged to maintain the role of mental patient.

Underlying all these points are the politics of deviance identification and control.[57] In any society there are key people whose job it is to identify and label deviant behaviour, e.g., policemen, doctors. These people perform their tasks largely in accordance with conventional social expectations. Many professionals come from the higher social classes and share the beliefs, prejudices or norms of those classes. People from lower social classes are often those who are labelled as deviant because they cannot resist the label which is being thrust upon them, e.g., hooligan, incompetent mother, mentally ill person.[58]

It helps enormously in avoiding a permanent attribution of deviance if you are an influential member of society.[59] Thus George III avoided the attribution of lunacy for many years because his social status was greater than that of his physicians. In our own time, the growing social and economic influence of homosexual people has helped to ensure that this condition is no longer officially regarded as an illness, which was the case for over a century. The point is that when you are dealing with disorders as elusive and invisible as mental disorders, there is great scope for making unfounded or dubious attributions.

This danger is enormously increased when those who are labelled have little power to change social values, to insist on social rights or to challenge the power and status of professionals who have a crucial role in determining their status. Once a person is labelled as mentally ill, there may be little chance of ditching the label. A famous study by Rosenham which gives an account of some social researchers who got themselves admitted to a psychiatric hospital but then behaved in perfectly normal ways is sobering in this respect. All the researchers continued to be regarded as ill by the hospital staff for a long time.[60] More recently, the English Parliamentary Ombudsman investigated the case of a young psychiatric patient who broke his leg and dragged himself round the hospital in agony for some weeks without being examined or treated by a doctor. The nurses and doctors in the hospital thought he was just pretending to be hurt and that this was simply a symptom of his mental disorder.

7. *Social Models* Social models of mental disorder take the general line that the incidence, progress and treatment of mental disorder owes a great deal to wider social and economic factors such as class position, social inequality, the nature of the social order etc. The prevention and cure of mental illness is then at least partly a matter of restructuring society. I want to explore this view more thoroughly below in relation to Christian responses to mental illness. First, however, some general observations about the perspectives on mental disorder and its treatment reviewed above.

One obvious but important point to make about the range of perspectives outlined is that there is simply no one 'right' way of looking at mental disorder. All the models described show up important aspects of what mental disorder and its treatment mean today. It is, therefore, crucial that no perspective should be adopted to the exclusion of all others. Despite the range and panoply of medical treatment of mentally ill people, for example, it must be remembered that the existence of disease entities which 'cause' mental illnesses cannot ultimately be proved. There must be times when other viewpoints are of greater utility than those of the medical model, both in understanding and in treating those perceived as mentally disordered. For example, understanding mental disorder as social deviance which attracts stigma and opprobrium might be more illuminating for ordinary people who have to cope with mentally disturbed people living in their midst, than trying to understand what is known of the biochemistry of medical treatments.

A corollary point is that, in practice, different models tend to be used eclectically anyway. Some models complement each other, e.g., those of custodialism and disease, community care and disease, and there is always a tendency amongst professionals to use any model or method which seems to produce results. This is not the place to discuss whether it is good or bad that models merge in this way, it is just important to point out that it happens.[61]

Where treatments have been ascribed to particular models and perspectives, it should be remembered that in almost every case there is a substantial amount of doubt as to how and whether they work. The history of psychiatry is littered with examples of therapeutic practices which have subsequently been discredited after the appearance of some initial success. The asylum movement, insulin coma therapy, psychotherapy and psychosurgery have all been hailed as universal panaceas, just as drugs and community care are today. The pattern seems to be that almost any new treatment initiative achieves some success with mentally ill people simply because it is new and excites enthusiasm, high morale and confidence among patients and therapists. It is probably the case that some patients are helped by some kinds of treatment, but universal prescription of a particular therapeutic agent has diminishing returns over the long term. The placebo effect is dissipated and many mentally disturbed people remain where they were before the treatment started, or perhaps in a worse state. If the roots of mental disorder are invisible and elusive, the value and effect of treatment is equally hard to gauge.

Finally, I want to underline the potential for repression and oppressive control which accompanies all types of psychiatric treatment. Care and control are always closely related.[62] Therapies for mental disorder are attempts at control of an undesirable condition and should be wanted by society, by professionals and by mentally ill people themselves. The trouble is that there is by no means always harmony and unity of purpose between these different parties. Sometimes, for example, mentally disordered people do not see themselves as having a problem and actively resist medical treatment (doubtless they are right to do so at times). In a situation of that kind, as well as in situations where resources and morale are lacking, it is all too easy for therapeutic measures to become a covert way of controlling patients. And because patients are relatively vulnerable and powerless, they may find it difficult to resist compulsory care.

In the next part of the chapter I will explore the impotence and vulnerability of mentally disordered people as a group more thoroughly. I want to suggest that Christian healing responses must give a primary place to socio-political perspectives on mental disorder and that they should embody a concrete option for the poor.

Mental Illness and 'the Poor'

One of the most exciting developments in Christian theology over the past two decades has been the emergence of theologies of liberation, particularly in so-called 'Third World' countries.[63] These theologies place a primary emphasis on the social and political dimensions of life and on the concrete struggle for freedom and liberation of the poor and dispossessed. Liberation theologies reject the preoccupation of Western theologies with individualism, personal piety and metaphysical speculation about the nature of God. They claim that the place where Christians should be and can engage in authentic theological activity is in direct political involvement alongside the poor. It is in the light of this perspective that I want to argue that mentally ill people should be seen as the poor in our society. Christian healing strategies in relation to them should, therefore, contain a large element of socio-political involvement and awareness. Mentally ill people are in a literal, not a metaphorical way the poor in contemporary British society. They are not only unfortunate individual sufferers; they comprise a group which is socially and economically dispossessed in every way. This assertion must be justified.

In the first place, mental illness sufferers come disproportionately from the lowest socio-economic classes. Although it is true that there are people who suffer from mental disorder in all social classes, this is one of the better established findings of social psychiatric research. Despite popular stereotypes that it is really only those with huge responsibilities in society, captains of industry and the like, who experience mental 'breakdowns', it is unfortunately the case that incidence of mental disorder is inversely related to social class position. It is not clear whether it is because they have a predisposition to mental illness that people actually drift downwards into the lowest social classes or whether conditions within those classes actually predispose to mental illness. A consensus of opinion tends to the latter view and it is hypothesized that the stresses of working class life married with a greater incidence of major traumatic life events, e.g., unemployment, and rigidity of world view leads to a higher incidence of mental illness.[64] Other factors may also contribute. For example, lower or working class people may be less able to get early treatment, they may be less able to resist being labelled as mentally ill by health professionals, and they may have less access to protective features such as paid and worthwhile employment. Whatever the exact causal connection between lower class life and mental disorder, it is quite clear that mental disorder is differentially distributed in British society to the disadvantage of the already disadvantaged.

Social class does not only affect the incidence of mental disorder. It is also significant in regard to speed of recovery, the quality and type of treatment facility used, length of hospital stay and long-term prognosis. People from lower social classes (of whom, as we have seen, there are a disproportionate number amongst the mentally ill) take longer to recover from episodes of illness, have fewer facilities and less good facilities for treatment, stay in hospital for longer if admitted for treatment and they have a poorer long term prognosis of avoiding future recurrences of their disorder.[65]

Women are a disadvantaged group in contemporary society in terms of influence, employment opportunities and economic power. At the same time, women are far more likely than men to experience mental disorder. While 11% of men are admitted to a psychiatric hospital in the course of their lives, the corresponding figure for women is 17%. Indeed, mental disorder has almost come to be regarded as a woman's disease; the human face of mental illness is female.[66] Once again, the reasons for this correlation between gender and mental disorder are obscure, but it seems likely that factors such as reduced choice, a lack of self esteem and a sense of hopelessness play a large part in making women vulnerable to mental illness.[67] Protective factors against mental disorder such as employment are often denied to women who may be tied to the home looking after dependent children or other relatives.

Race may also be a significant variable in determining whether or not mental disorder is experienced and how it is dealt with. A recent study in South London demonstrated that black people were more likely to be diagnosed as mentally ill and treated in secure psychiatric units than white people.[68] Whether this was because of ignorance, racism or simply because black people are more prone to mental disorder is not clear, but once again it is evidence of the differential social distribution of perceived mental disorder which seems to affect disadvantaged groups in society in general more than, say, white upper middle class males.

There is some evidence to suggest that unemployment adversely affects mental health and it has been argued that economic recession spawns mental illness in its wake amongst those who lose their jobs and fall into financial difficulties.[69] It is, of course, people in the lower social classes who are most adversely affected by economic recession and unemployment. Here, then, is a further straw which points to the differential distribution of mental disorder against the interests of the disadvantaged.

One very important group of mentally ill people is that of the elderly mentally ill. It is reckoned that by the year 2001 there will be two million people over the age of 80 in the UK and that over a fifth of them will suffer from dementia of some kind.[70] Already almost half the beds devoted to mental illness in the Health Service are taken up by the elderly mentally ill.[71] Many of these people suffer from Alzheimer's disease, a condition which cannot be directly correlated with social class position or economic, racial and gender factors. This should not lead to the conclusion that there are no social and political connotations to mental illness amongst the elderly. The fact is that elderly people in our society are almost by definition poor, powerless and uninfluential:

> The elderly make up such a substantial proportion of the poor that the question is posed whether poverty can be explained as the problem of old age.[72]

Mentally ill people as a group, whatever their individual social backgrounds, are severely disadvantaged in terms of social influence and power. Society as a whole has little interest in them. Mentally ill people themselves have almost no purchase on the main political and economic structures ordering society. Economically, they produce very little and have almost no money to spend. Strikes and boycotts are therefore not means which can be used to attract attention to their grievances. Politically, mentally ill people are not sufficiently well-organized to lobby policy makers effectively. Until recently, indeed, many patients in psychiatric hospitals were actually ineligible to exercise one of the basic rights of citizenship, that of voting in elections for public office. Generally, mentally ill people have substantially reduced rights and opportunities and their protests can be interpreted as symptoms of their disorder and dealt with by threats of compulsory detention and treatment, or simply by being ignored.[73] The relative social and political impotence of mentally ill people and their associates is eloquently summarized by an American writer:

> Mental patients do not write letters to their state representatives or to newspapers; they do not picket or demonstrate in front of state capitols . . . As opposed to labor, business and the professions . . . they are almost completely powerless to affect the political process. Even compared to other have-not groups – alcoholics, prisoners, or welfare mothers – they have no clout . . . The mentally ill do not have . . . a body of mentally intact relatives, due to the complex socio-environmental and genetic etiology of serious mental illness . . . As a result *they constitute one of the truly powerless constituencies in our society.*[74]

Mentally ill people are the poor in terms of class, status, finance, and influence. The depth of their relative deprivation is highlighted by the inadequacy of the resources spent on their care within the National Health Service. Clare reports that in 1976, 43% of all patients in English hospitals were in mental illness beds. At the same time only 11% of all consultants were psychiatrists and only 20% of nurses worked in psychiatry. Psychiatric consultants had to look after an average of 154 in-patients as opposed to the 30 which was average for consultants in acute specialities. In hospitals for the mentally ill there were 36 nurses for every 100 patients while in non-psychiatric hospitals there were 121 nurses for every 100 patients. The average cost of maintaining a patient in an acute ward was just under £90 while only £30 was spent on patients in psychiatric facilities.[75]

At its worst, the lack of care, attention and resources devoted to the mentally ill has produced terrible demoralization and concommitant cruelty and neglect. A touchstone of just how bad things can get for mentally ill people, is to be found in the reports of enquiries into old psychiatric hospitals in the 1970s.[76] At one hospital, for example, the following allegations were found proven by a commission of enquiry. Patients were sworn at and hit around the head, as well as being threatened by one nurse. One patient was slapped for not urinating. Electro-convulsive therapy (ECT) was given to an unwilling voluntary patient (i.e., a patient who was not compulsorily detained under the provisions of the Mental Health Act) who had to be manhandled to be made to comply. Another patient was kept locked in a bare, smelly side room for a month. Psychogeriatric patients on some wards received baths only very infrequently. Patients' property and presents brought for them were denied them. They were deprived of their spectacles and had little opportunity to engage in any kind of stimulating activity. Patients did not receive the pocket money to which they were entitled. On one ward, patients were deprived of liquid if they were incontinent. Sometimes patients were made to 'perform' in front of groups of students by a charge nurse. Clothing supplies were inadequate (a very serious problem when dealing with repeatedly incontinent patients). One charge nurse deprived a patient of food for several weeks. Some patients were verbally abused and openly called 'dumbos' by nurses. One patient was kept in his pyjamas and dressing gown for nine months. Some patients almost never saw their doctors and a patient was given ECT without first being physically examined by a doctor. It became apparent subsequently that she was not fit enough to have this treatment.[77]

The sort of conditions described above are anything but therapeutic. Although many of the old psychiatric hospitals are now being closed, it seems problematic as to whether things will really be better for mentally ill people experiencing community care. Provision of day care and hostel facilities lags well behind demand and it is often far from ideal.[78] Patients often end up living in inadequate hostel accommodation, rented accommodation in the twilight areas of cities or even on the long stay wards of the streets. These are not promising settings for recovery from mental illness and rehabilitation into the main structures of society. Sadly, the Government has recently decided to reduce the budget for community care yet further.[79] Protests against this from mentally ill people and the electorate have been so muted as to be almost inaudible.[80] Given what I have already said about the mentally ill as an oppressed group of poor people, this is unfortunately entirely predictable.

Towards a Contemporary Christian Response to Mental Disorder

Given the large numbers of mentally ill people in our midst with their varying needs and situations, the diversity of perspectives and modes of treatment which are available, and the capacities of different individuals and groups, Christian healing responses to mental disorder must themselves be variegated. They might range

from praying with individuals and offering various kinds of distinctively religious healing to them, through to providing accommodation and day care facilities in a local church. But if Christians
are truly concerned that people should not become mentally ill,
and if they do that, they should get the kind of treatment which
will maximize their opportunities for recovery and re-entry into
the community at large, their healing responses must also have a
social and political dimension to them.

Although it is not at all clear why people in lower social classes,
women and black people are more vulnerable to mental disorder
than the white male ruling classes, it is clear by inference that there
are gross inequalities here. In some ways, the latter group are
protected from illness by their station in life and the opportunities
it provides. A Christian healing response must therefore be set
within a wider struggle for a just society in which stress and
opportunity are more equally spread. Similarly, a comprehensive
Christian healing response to mental disorder should include a
determination to highlight the needs and deprivations of mentally
ill people in the eyes of the public and the Government. The
mentally ill are the poor. They cannot fight for themselves on their
own. They need the interest of relatively powerful groups like the
churches who have a determination to struggle with them for their
welfare and to help them articulate their demands. We do not know
much about mental disorder, how it is caused, or how it can be
cured. What is apparent is that there is an important social and
political dimension to it. This should be vigorously worked on
through the democratic structures of change in society.

Since the decline of 'religious madness' in the eighteenth century
Christians have shown relatively little interest in mental illness.
While there have been honourable exceptions to this lack of interest
such as Tuke, Shaftesbury and Elly Jansen (the founder of the
Richmond Fellowship), on the whole Christians like the rest of
society have tended to behave as if the mentally ill were not
there. They have allowed them to become invisible. No major
denomination in England has produced any kind of report or policy
statement on mental illness and the place of the mentally ill in our
society. With the exception of occasional flurries of interest in
exorcism and the paranormal, there is nothing but a deafening
silence. The hard task of healing the mentally ill and the structures
which conspire to make and keep them sick is one which needs to

be addressed urgently. If the same kind of interest and vigour which has spawned and sustained the hospice movement could be applied to the equally great needs of mentally ill people, a real and necessary change could be wrought in society. It is not so much death and cancer which are our contemporary social taboos; it is the perennial and all too common phenomenon of mental illness.[81]

Chapter Six

The Judgment of AIDS[1]

'AIDS has threatened our sense of medical security.'[2]

This almost matter-of-fact sounding statement from medical historian Allan Brandt apparently belies the reality of which it speaks, the most serious crisis which the human race in the West has faced since the last World War. AIDS challenges humanity at all levels of existence, from that of governmental policy making to that of the suffering of the individual. All sorts of assumptions, beliefs and behaviours have become very problematic. Life will never again be the same for anyone with this mysterious, horrifying and incurable condition around.

In a real sense, AIDS brings judgment on our society. In a fundamental and devastating way, it shows up the nature of individuals and institutions for what they really are. Writing of the impact of the plague on Tudor and Stuart England, Paul Slack captures the essence of this sense of judgment:

> Sudden disastrous events such as epidemics illuminate many facets of the societies with which they collide. They create situations of stress which test the institutions, and the habits of mind and behaviour, which normally hold society together.[3]

Judging and Being Judged

AIDS brings judgment on society. But society and the individuals who comprise it must also judge AIDS as well as being judged by it. They must work out their attitudes and responses to it. It is this mutual double judgment which forms the main theme of this chapter. Judgment is a very familiar concept in Christianity. The perceived close association of AIDS with morality, sex and death is, however, a particularly rich context of ambiguity, difficulty and confusion in which Christians have to begin to develop appropriate understandings.

To start with AIDS itself. The syndrome is a curious one in that it does not actually kill people itself; it allows them to become vulnerable to other conditions which may prove fatal, by interfering with the body's auto-immune system. Mercifully, AIDS is relatively difficult to contract being transmitted only by direct contact with the body fluids of an infected person. This makes the main channels of infection sexual intercourse or other sexual contact of various kinds, direct contact with open sores of wounds, sharing hypodermic needles, or transfusion with infected blood. The symptoms of the condition take some time to develop, so people who have it do not necessarily know that they have it; this is surely one of the most sinister and difficult aspects of AIDS. At the time of writing (summer 1988), in the UK only a few hundred people have developed the condition in its full form, but their number is sure to multiply many times in the next few years.[4] Although many of those who have contracted AIDS in the UK and North America have either been homosexuals or illicit drug users, there is a significant number of haemophiliacs who have contracted AIDS through transfusion with contaminated blood supplies.[5] Expectant mothers can transmit the condition directly to their foetuses. While AIDS has been labelled a 'gay plague' it is important to realize that, world-wide, the majority of those affected by it are heterosexual. It seems likely that heterosexuals will outnumber homosexual sufferers in the UK within a very short time.

There is some debate on the question of where AIDS originated, how, when, and why? It was first diagnosed as a distinctive discrete syndrome in the USA in 1981. There is no cure as yet for the condition, and none is expected in the immediate future. Although it is possible that, like other great epidemics, AIDS might run itself out or spontaneously disappear, it seems probable that it will be around for a long time to come, just like syphylis which was incurable for centuries after its introduction into Europe. The only relatively good news that can be reported is that research is progressing, some alleviatory drugs may have been discovered, expertise in caring for those who contract AIDS is growing and, so far, relatively few people out of the whole population have contracted the syndrome. There can be no doubt, however, that things looks very grim for the immediate future. All parts of society are going to feel the scourge of AIDS. Individuals with AIDS are going to have to endure possibly years of physical discomfort, uncertainty and guilt. Most people are going to have to witness friends and relations coping with the condition. Social and industrial institutions are going to lose key people. The economy will suffer both from lost working days and from the extra expense which will be incurred in providing extra health care facilities for AIDS sufferers. The National Health Service will be even further stretched than it is at the moment in providng extra help and care. Unlikely as it may still seem to some, everyone is going to be adversely affected by AIDS.[6]

The Role of Government

The Government has chosen to handle AIDS on a pragmatic basis as a matter of public health and health education. In a pluralist, secular society, it has abstained from drawing morals or offering advice about values to the population. It has advocated practical measures like sticking to one partner, using adequate safety measures if more than one partner is envisaged, and in the case of drug users, not sharing hypodermic needles.

Here, then, is the first matter for Christian judgment. Is the Government right to take a clinical, 'neutral' approach to the spread of AIDS? Whatever conclusion may be drawn, it is very important to take into account the fact that the Government has a duty to protect people of all persuasions and none against a deadly condition in an absolutely realistic way. It has to be recognized that extra-marital sexual relationships are a major feature of our society (as they have been of many societies since time began). It simply will not do for a government, which represents the interests of all the people, to uphold and appeal to values which are held only by a small minority of the population. The revolution in sexual behaviour and attitudes which has occured in the present century leaves Christians in a very difficult position, which they have yet to address adequately; how is it possible to proclaim a distinctive Christian sexual ethic which is utterly realistic about the evolving and uncertain development of patterns of sexual relationship today?

For some, the answer to this question is to reiterate the teaching of the tradition, to recall fellow citizens to verities which are believed to have withstood the test of time and to have divine sanction. Although this witness has much to be said for it, the trouble is that it does almost nothing to reach the hearts and attitudes of those who do not already agree with it. It is essential that Christians should give a great deal of thought to the way in which they might evolve and set forth ethical ideals while being sensitive and realistic about the limits of their appeal. In the face of AIDS, there is little scope for pious hope or wishful thinking in regard to human behaviour. Because of their own experience of evil, sin, grace and forgiveness, Christians should be sympathetic to what they may perceive to be the evil-doing and frailty of others. They will be loath to see neighbours within and outside the church community suffering the full and awful effects of AIDS even if it appears that they are suffering as a result of their own misdeeds. Perhaps, then, there are factors which should lead Christians to largely support the present governmental strategy, despite its apparent lack of religious moral ideals.

Getting AIDS into Proportion

The second area for Christian judgment concerns the amount of energy and interest which should be given to AIDS. The novelty of this epidemic, the relatively large amount of publicity which has been given to it by Government and media and the advent of the first people with AIDS in this country have resulted in a great deal of attention from the churches. This is very appropriate up to a point; Christians should be concerned about bodies as well as souls. But while not in any way wishing to diminish concern for AIDS and those who have it, it must be remembered that many other diseases afflict our population in epidemic proportions; cancer and heart disease are but the most obvious examples. The difference between these diseases and AIDS is that often a great deal more is known about their causes, prevention and cure, though relatively little is done in practice to implement the knowledge which exists in theory. Each week 275 people die of smoking related diseases, many more die in road accidents caused by drunken driving. It is certainly important to respond directly and positively to AIDS, but there are other causes of death and destruction in our society which could also be responded to in effective ways. The response to AIDS should form part of a much broader and more long-standing strategy for combatting bodily disease and disorder in general.

AIDS as Punishment for Sin

The most controversial aspect of the advent of AIDS from a religious point of view has been the suggestion that this condition is a punishment for human sin, especially sexual immorality, particularly homosexual immorality. This response to sudden and otherwise inexplicable disaster on a grand scale is an ancient and classic one.[7] It seems to have a great deal to do with finding meaning, explanation and control amidst chaos.[8] Clearly, all sorts of complex issues are at stake here. For example, is God the sort of God who intervenes in the natural and social order? Does he intervene directly or indirectly? Does the universe run on a simple model of cause and effect whereby specific human behaviour automatically produces a reciprocal effect.[9] And what place does wrath or punishment have in the nature of a loving God who is held to reveal himself supremely in the life and ministry of Jesus?[10] There are no easy or quick answers to these questions. There are, however, some important factors which must be taken into account when considering them in relation to AIDS.

First, what is to be made of the fact that not only the 'guilty' but also the 'innocent' in the form of unborn children, spouses of people with AIDS and people with haemophilia suffer from the condition?

Secondly, while the Old Testament in parts certainly seems to advance the view that people get their just deserts for evil-doing and immorality in the form of illness and misfortune, the ministry of Jesus seems to point towards an implacable enmity to disease however it may be caused. The New Testament writers portray Jesus as taking no satisfaction in seeing people suffer the conse-quences of their own or others' sins. Jesus rejects diagnosis, the apportioning of blame and the attribution of meaning in illness in favour of forgiveness and practical compassionate healing.[11]

Thirdly, although it may be comforting in some ways to regard the universe as running along clear lines of wrong-doing bringing about punishment, one of the main thrusts of the Christian tradition would seem to be that people do *not* get what they deserve in terms of punishment. We live within the grace of God in a gracious and loving universe. We are forgiven and do not take the consequence of our evil actions. If the world was an absolutely just place and God an unswervingly just judge who related to humanity according to a rule book, presumably we should all have AIDS; not because of our sexual immorality perhaps (this is a minor concern in biblical ethical thought), but because we in the West consistently ignore the needs of the poor and weak in favour of our own self interest (a major concern in biblical ethics). As it is, AIDS is working its most diabolical effects amongst heterosexuals in the poorest countries of the world in Africa and elsewhere. What have people done there to deserve 'punishment' of this sort?

Fourthly, to maintain that people are justly punished for their immorality by contracting AIDS leads logically to the position that nothing should be done to help them. If God has brought punishment upon them, they should be allowed to suffer it until God chooses to remove it. Although there is a long-standing tradition in Christianity that accords with this view (exemplified, for example, in the Visitation of the Sick rite in the *Book of Common Prayer*), it is difficult to want to exalt this as being a primary stance today. The concept of AIDS as a punishment may help to make sense of a frightening and otherwise apparently purposeless phenomenon, but it must be deeply problematic for Christians who see God more as loving Father rather than as arbitrary destroyer.

AIDS and Traditional Christian Values

A debate about morality has been opened up by the advent of AIDS. Some church leaders have come very close to suggesting that AIDS in some way 'proves' that traditional Christian values of heterosexual monogamy were right all along. After years of seeing Christian sexual ethics devalued and despised, it is tempting to see them as now vindicated by a kind of 'natural law' which shows that straying from divinely sanctioned historic norms brings disaster.

Several observations need to be made here. In the first place,

morality, if it is to be dignified with that title at all, must be a
matter of free rational choice. Appeals to fear, punishment,
reward or coercion reduce morality to enforced conformity.[12] The
legitimate ideals of the church vis à vis sexual relations and family
life should commend themselves as an attractive and worthwhile
vision to rational adults who freely assent to them and adopt them.
They should not be forced upon people with appeals to subliminal
fear, guilt and punishment for non-conformity. God draws people
to himself and his ways in love; this allows them free will. He does
not coerce them against their better judgment.

It is also necessary to point up the danger of Christians becoming
moralistic. Many may feel that, actually, AIDS has very little to
do with them. They do not indulge in practices which might make
them vulnerable to infection, neither do their family, friends,
neighbours or co-religionists. It is relatively easy in this situation
to have a strict personal moral code and to expect others to do the
same. The trouble is that this can appear merciless and unforgiving
to those who are not themselves Christians and to Christians who
have 'lapsed'. The temptation to moral superiority or indifference
must be resisted. Beneath the surface of some of the concerned
responses from church leaders for people with AIDS it has sometimes been possible to detect patronizing attitudes and even
some echoes of satisfaction that evil-doers are receiving their just
recompense. Against this, I would suggest that any morality which
makes 'good' and respectable people feel better at the expense of
making the outcast and suffering feel worse and more rejected
must be suspect amongst the followers of a man who mixed freely
with sinners and eventually died outside a city wall branded as a
criminal.[13]

Lastly, church leaders are often accused of being soft and of
refusing to lay down traditional moral guidelines vociferously and
forcefully. The question here is, 'Who really benefits from this
kind of exhortation?' Doubtless the faithful and conforming will
be re-assured and confirmed in their own behaviours and attitudes.
But it seems uncertain whether the proclamation of this sort reaches
or challenges the unconverted and outcast. Telling people off and
punishing them is a very poor way of getting people to change.[14]
What does change them is love and acceptance. Love is a word
which has gone out of fashion in Christian ethics and other parts
of church life since the 1960s. Perhaps we no longer believe that it

is possible to love or to change and be changed through loving in the 1980s. If so, we need to remind ourselves that Jesus' primary and impossible command was that we should love as he loves us. When there is too much love and acceptance of people who perceive themselves to be outcast and rejected in Christian communities, let us by all means call for more condemnation of sinners and sin. In the meanwhile there is the very practical task of ridding ourselves of a sense of moral superiority so that the outcast can feel real warmth of acceptance.

Learning from the Past

So far, most of what has been said has been concerned with Christian judgment of AIDS. At the beginning of the chapter, however, it was asserted that AIDS also judges society, social and religious institutions and individuals in that it shows them up for what they really are. Turning to this theme now more directly, an interesting if tangential way of tackling it and throwing it into relief is to look at responses to epidemic diseases in the past.

In Philip Ziegler's account of the plague of 1348, *The Black Death*, a fascinating variety of different attitudes and responses can be seen.[15] At the top of the social hierarchy, the Pope of the day completely withdrew himself from the world and human contact to sit between two large fires in his Avignon palace until the plague outbreak subsided. For him, the most important thing was to ensure his own survival. His example was imitated by many of the bishops. They either locked themselves into their residences or fled their dioceses altogether. Most people in mediaeval society believed the plague to be in some way the action of God, but at a practical level there was a considerable divergence of response. Some resorted to such natural medicaments as they believed to be effective. Others maintained that physical means were hopeless. The only way to escape a divinely inflicted punishment was to reform the social institutions such as brothels which had angered the Almighty. There were some who drew exactly the opposite practical conclusion from the same theological premises; if the wrath of God was being inflicted upon the whole of society, there could be no escape so why not eat, drink and indulge in debauchery until death struck you down?

A widespread attitude was to try and identify some groups of individuals who could be blamed for bringing plague on the whole of society and who could be scapegoated. Predictably, the Jews provided an easy target for this, but all social outsiders were vulnerable to being assigned this unenviable role and the persecution which accompanied it. Some people believed that if they performed expiatory religious rites on behalf of the whole of society such as public penance, pilgrimage or fasting, this would avert the wrath of God.

One gratifying and positive response was witnessed in the behaviour of some of the lower clergy who insisted on staying in the plague-infested parishes with complete disregard to their own safety. Similar altruism was sometimes to be found in whole communities which put themselves into voluntary quarantine. But this was paralleled in many places by an absolute determination on the part of individual citizens not to let their lives, purposes and interests be affected by public quarantine regulations.[16]

History has moved on and twentieth-century people have a very different context together with different understandings of God and disease. Nonetheless, we find ourselves faced by a similar crisis and some of the attitudes described have instructive similarities to our own. Disinterest, self-interest, indifference, immorality, moral righteousness, blame, hatred, scapegoating, concern, social solidarity and selfless service are all as much possibilities for us as they were six hundred years ago. We, too, must decide how we are going to respond to AIDS and those who contract it. It is a judgment we cannot avoid.

Responding to AIDS

There are several levels at which Christians might begin to respond to AIDS. These are (1) Knowledge and perception of AIDS; (2) practical help and support for people with AIDS, their families and friends; (3) theological reflection.

1. Knowledge and perception of AIDS   Despite the media coverage of AIDs, many people remain profoundly ignorant of the syndrome, its causes and effects. While it is true that most Christians are probably still unaffected by the syndrome, it is important that they should learn about it, both as a prelude to direct helping responses and also with a view to creating the right kind of ideological environment in society against which appropriate helping responses can be made.

As I said at the beginning of this chapter, AIDS has become embroiled in a complex but implicit debate about attitudes to morality, sex and death. It seems as if AIDS acts as a kind of ventriloquist's dummy through which people say important and difficult things about sex, morality and a variety of other issues. Metaphors and personifications of AIDS abound. Thus it can be construed as a punishment, as a sexual disease, as a disease with no moral connotations whatsoever, even, as I have represented it here, as a kind of entity which judges us. This underlines a point I made right at the beginning of the book, that we have no direct access to the reality of disease, we only have a variety of competing views and interpretations.[17]

These competing views and interpretations are filled with social values and presuppose very different solutions. If AIDS is perceived as a punishment for moral degenerates, for example, it may make it easy and desirable to believe that these evil-doers should be locked up so that they do not infect other people with their wicked ways and disorders. If it is thought of as a disease without moral connotations, the solution is to try and protect people from contracting it, whatever the personal habits, and to try and find a cure for it. The language and concepts used about AIDS are often emotive and value-laden. We owe it to people who have or may contract AIDS to think very carefully about our perception of it. What we think, and the words we use, will affect the sort of treatment and attitudes adopted by society as a whole.

In this connection, it may be necessary for Christians to think very carefully about their own attitudes to sexuality, death and disease.[18] It seems vital that a syndrome which is transmitted by blood and other body fluids should not become a platform for moral objections to the behaviour of others, without it being quite clear that the syndrome is being co-opted for ulterior motives, such as objecting strongly to homosexuality. It might be much more honest to say that we hate homosexuals, than to dress up our distaste for their lifestyle in psuedo-medical concern. A concern for concepts, perceptions, attitudes, language and moral ventriloquism will allow us to care about, and be in solidarity with, those who have AIDS, their families and friends, even if we never ever meet somebody with the syndrome.

2. Practical help and support   AIDS is a mysterious syndrome. Those who have it may not realize that they have it. When they do realize, they will be uncertain as to when it will become full-blown and how they will react. They will not know if, and when they are going to die. They may worry that they have passed the syndrome on to others. There is plenty of room here for anguish, guilt, loneliness, bereavement, stigmatization and fear, quite apart from the sheer long-term physical disability which the syndrome may engender. Relatives and friends, too, will have to cope with a complex and physically and emotionally draining situation.

There is, then, much scope for friendship, pastoral concern, counselling and support. Perhaps, above all, for the unjudgmental love to which Christianity is supposed to aspire. There is beginning to be a substantial literature on how to give practical help to people with AIDS and those around them. Interested readers can explore this further through the references in the note.[19]

3. Theological reflection   Technological, medical and social advances in the West over the last hundred years or so have disguised the vulnerability of human beings to disease. We are, therefore, ill-prepared to cope with the judgment of AIDS. Much of the immediate reaction to this condition has been founded upon the natural but dangerous human reaction of fear. A re-stated Christian theology of fear is badly needed in our time. Such a theology cannot be offered here, but some seeds for its development may be found in two historical examples.

When Christianity was in its early phase, it is recorded that one of the remarkable things about Christians was that they did not flee the cities in which they lived when plagues struck. Because of their trust in God and their lack of fear of death, Christians stayed among their dying fellows and ministered to them in a remarkable show of faith, compassion and solidarity. This evidence of the triumph of faith over fear is also found in Athanasius' central proof for the resurrection of Christ in his treatise, *De Incarnatione*. Instead of arguing about the historicity of the gospel witness or arguing abstruse philosophical points, Athanasius vindicates the reality of resurrection by pointing to the behaviour and attitudes of contemporary Christians:

A very strong proof of this destruction of death and its conquest by the cross is supplied by a present fact, namely this. All the disciples of Christ despise death; they take the offensive against it and, instead of fearing it, by the sign of the cross and by faith in Christ trample on it as on something dead.[20]

The attempt to rediscover and re-interpret something of the spirit of early Christians in their rejection of fear would seem to be a very important project for Christians concerned about AIDS today. We must find new and realistic grounds for hope which are appropriate to our time.

Conclusion

Doubtless, contemporary Christians can argue doctrinal niceties until the Second Coming. It is their response and attitude to the fear, suffering and death brought about by AIDS, amongst other diseases, which will prove the truth and relevance of the gospel for this generation. There are great opportunities for witnessing to the power of love, compassion and solidarity here. Equally, there is the possibility of isolation, moralistic indifference and complacency at the expense of people with AIDS and their families. I conclude with a second quote from Allan Brandt who not only encapsulates the judgment of AIDS on society and individuals, but also reminds of the importance of illness in general as a testing point for beliefs, institutions and practices:

> We will . . . learn a great deal about the nature of our society [and church – SP] from the manner in which we address the disease. AIDS will be a measure upon which we may calibrate not only our medical and scientific skill but our capacity for justice and compassion.[21]

Afterword

Right at the beginning of this book, I promised that there would be no conclusion. This was because of the nature of the work. My aim has been to point up the need for a deeper engagement with the nature of illness and healing and to invite readers to reflect on their own perceptions of the nature of these things. I hope I have shown that there are any number of possible directions for fruitful exploration. I also hope I may have provided some clues about ways of commencing investigation and that some of my readers will now take up where I have left off.

For their sake, as well as for the sake of those who may now be thinking, 'Well, that was all very interesting, but what have I really learned from it in practical terms and where do I go from here?', I want, finally, simply to list some of the questions arising from the contents of this text. Readers may find it profitable to apply them to beliefs and practices concerned with illness and healing whether their own or those of others.

1. Who decides, and who should decide, what illness and healing are?

2. What is the nature of the recognition and decision-making process in relation to illness and healing?

3. Does anyone 'benefit' from current patterns of morbidity and mortality? Does anyone lose out by the way that illness and healing are recognized, organized and distributed?

4. What are the knowledge and language systems which are used to talk about and deal with illness and healing? Which systems are to be regarded as normative? Why?

5. Which systems are regarded as suspect or invalid? Why are they so regarded?

6. Whose perspectives on illness and healing are completely ignored?

7. Do different perspectives and practices complement each other, or do they conflict? What is the nature of their complementarity/conflict?

8. In any particular instance or situation of illness, what attitudes and explanations are adopted with regard to cause, effect, responsibility, God? What is the context of these explanations? What purpose do they serve, implicitly or explicitly? Are different explanations given to different interlocutors? Why?

9. What is/should be the relationship between those perceived as sick and healing systems/healers?

10. What should Christian healing responses be in the contemporary world? Which factors, insights, perspectives and information should they take into account?

11. In relation to specific situations of illness, are Christian healing responses anachronistic, too narrow, too generalized, or too simplistic?

12. Are Christian healing responses situated within a wider search for justice and healing for society as a whole? Or do they overtly/covertly support an ideology of individualism and injustice?

13. Are Christian healing responses sensitive to God's purpose and work in the whole of creation with all people? How do they fit in with other therapeutic systems and understandings?

14. Do our various healing responses help people or damage them? How do we know? How might we find out?

15. How, if at all, do issues of conflict and power impinge upon healing systems and situations of illness?

16. Which values and power relationships are affirmed or denied by particular perspectives on illness and healing and the practices which are associated with them?

There are, of course, no easy, immediate or comprehensive answers to these questions. That does not mean that they are not worth asking or exploring. The attempt to do this will, I hope, lead to more appropriate and committed Christian healing responses to disease and disorder today.

I want to conclude by quoting some words which I find both intemperate and inspiring. They come from the Personal Epilogue to Antonio Perez Esclarin's *Atheism and Liberation* (SCM Press

1980), a book on the theology of liberation. They are both appalling and appealing. I think they bear repetition at the end of a rather abstract book like this:

> My readers, if there are any readers, will probably find this book hasty, unequal, and poorly worked out. I must confess that while I was writing it, I felt an enormous desire to leave it in mid-course. I felt that these were just words, more words, when the only worthwhile thing is committed personal action with the people. I finished the book hurriedly, overcoming myself continually, thinking that perhaps it might help someone after all. I feel no desire at all to go back over it and touch it up. Furthermore, I want these lines to be my final goodbye to the intellectual world. I have felt its attractions, but I think I have discovered its phoniness. Every idea is hollow if it is not fleshed out in real life. I don't really know whether the book I have written is of any value. But as for myself, I am going to try and live out its contents with the oppressed.

Perspectives on Illness: A Kaleidoscope A Diagrammatic Representation of Chapter 2

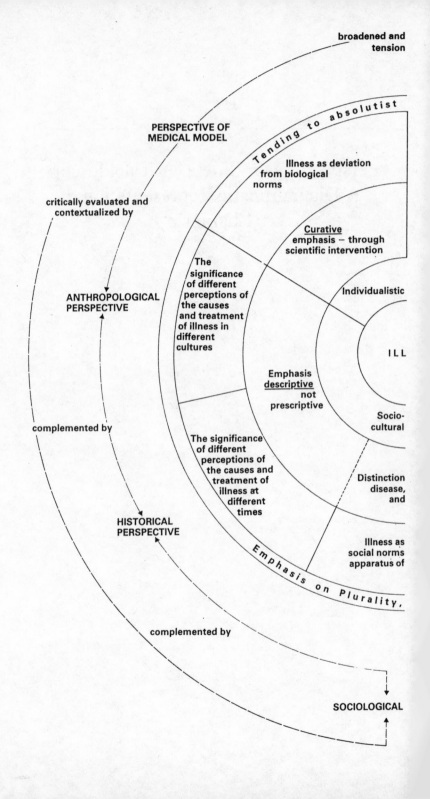

broadened and
tension

PERSPECTIVE OF
MEDICAL MODEL

Tending to absolutist

Illness as deviation
from biological
norms

Curative
emphasis — through
scientific intervention

critically evaluated and
contextualized by

Individualistic

ANTHROPOLOGICAL
PERSPECTIVE

The
significance
of different
perceptions of
the causes
and treatment
of illness in
different
cultures

ILL

Emphasis
descriptive
not
prescriptive

complemented by

Socio-
cultural

The significance
of different
perceptions of
the causes and
treatment of
illness at
different
times

Distinction
disease,
and

HISTORICAL
PERSPECTIVE

Illness as
social norms
apparatus of

Emphasis on Plurality,

complemented by

SOCIOLOGICAL

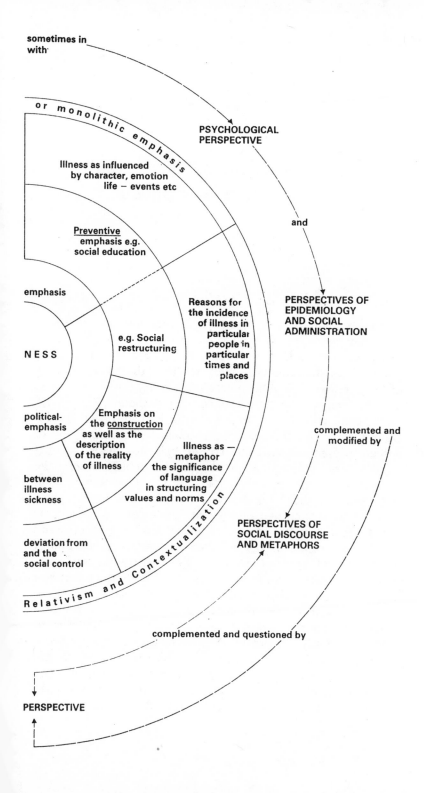

Medico-Religious Dialogue and Co-operation: an Epilogue?

It is a commonplace to observe that throughout the two millennia of the Christian era both religion and medicine have been actively concerned with the alleviation of disease and distress. The starting point for Christian attention to this area lies in the healing ministry of Jesus himself.[1] Until the nineteenth century it was common to find ministers of the church using natural and/or spiritual and sacramental means to restore suffering individuals to health.[2] Indeed, until this time clerics attempted (with a good deal of success) to dominate and control the health sector. Medieval popes regulated the practice of medicine so that it would best serve the interests and work of the church and even after the Reformation in England a bishop's license was required to practise as a physician.[3] It seems likely that the afflicted themselves took a pragmatic attitude to the various remedies, spiritual and other, on offer and resorted to doctors, clergy or other healers on the criterion of practical effectiveness.[4] Claims to clerical control and dominance within the health sector faded, along with the clerical practice of medicine, in the middle of the last century when doctors established themselves as a powerful self-regulating professional group in society.[5] The same historical era also witnessed the relinquishment of many diverse social and welfare roles by the clergy to specialize more directly in spiritual matters.[6] This process, which has continued into the present century, has brought about the effective subordination of clergy within the health sector. While Christian ministers continue to be present within the sphere of health care and treatment they now occupy an inferior and relatively unimportant position and the hospitals and those who work in them are now controlled by the doctors. A Dutch writer on hospital chaplaincy, Faber, encapsulates this point: 'The minister has his own task, with which the medical staff have little to do, but he is exercising this task in the domain of the doctor and stands within the hierarchy of which the latter is the head'.[7] In the present age there has never been any serious suggestion that this situation should be reversed so that clergy may resume their domination in the health sector. In the 1960s and 1970s, however, there were moves to establish close co-operation and dialogue between medicine and theology, between clergy and doctors. It is this development, and more particularly its apparent decline and its future prospects which will be the subject of consideration in this Appendix.

That there was a movement towards increased medico-theological co-operation and dialogue in the past two decades is not in doubt. The 1960s saw the establishment of clergy-doctor associations in many towns and cities in this country.[8] At the same time the Institute of Religion and Medicine was inaugurated and some outstanding senior doctors and clergymen became involved in its activities, e.g. Bishops Michael Ramsay and Ian Ramsey, physicians Sir John Stallworthy and Lord Porritt. The later part of the decade also witnessed the rise of the Medical Groups where matters of ethical concern could be discussed on a multidisciplinary basis. Though not all those involved in the medical groups were clergy, doctors, or Christians these constituencies were well represented in the activities of the Medical Groups as they evolved. At the educational level there was also a flurry of activity in the 1960s with the establishment of the Birmingham University Diploma in Pastoral Studies in 1964. The course was conceived and directed by the theologically qualified doctor, R. A. Lambourne, and was specifically designed to have a beneficial effect on mental and social health.[9] In the literary sphere Lambourne, together with Wilson, another medically qualified theologian and clergy like Melinsky and others provided a critical rationale for the involvement and co-operation of main stream Christianity with modern scientific medicines.[10] While the writing of books and articles and the inception of courses, groups and institutes may not give any real picture of everyday co-operation and dialogue 'on the ground', it seems fair to conclude that they must in some way reflect a groundswell of interest and activity at a practical level. In the psychiatric sector, for example, innovations like therapeutic communities and community psychiatry encouraged the active participation of 'lay' people and so may well have facilitated co-operation and dialogue between clergy and doctors as well as other health workers.[11] More recently, concern about ethical matters and particular groups of patients, e.g. the dying, may have promoted dialogue and co-operation between clergy and doctors in non-psychiatric areas of the health sector.

There are indicators that the era of medico-clerical dialogue and co-operation is now coming to an end. Many local clergy-doctor associations, founded with such vigour and optimism twenty or more years ago are now defunct or rapidly becoming so. The chairman of the Institute of Religion and Medicine's council has recently noted that the membership in 1983 is now about half what it was in 1971 when it was at its peak. Institute field groups at local level have declined from a peak of forty groups meeting in 1971.[12]

While there are distinguished theologians like Archbishop Habgood and Alastair Campbell still contributing to debates in medical ethics, these thinkers and others devote little of their energy specifically to dialogue and co-operation between clergy and doctors. No major writers of the stature of Ian Ramsey or R. A. Lambourne have been working in this area recently. Medical contributions to *Contact* have become less frequent and those which have been submitted over the last decade have come principally from the pens of two psychiatrists, Lake and Mathers. The Birmingham Diploma in Pastoral Studies has diversified beyond the confines of mental and social health and now has many non-ministers as its students. Outwith the main arena of medico-theological dialogue and co-operation the Medical Groups are failing and some have ceased operation altogether. It seems probable that at the level of practical everyday co-operation some individuals are working closely together. Clergy working within the parochial and health sectors have recently been able to confirm my own recent experience that doctors are largely indifferent, or even hostile to the clergy they encounter. Acceptance, co-operation and dialogue may be offered by particular doctors to individual clerics who have proved their usefulness and worth, but they are not available to clergy as a group. The foregoing points are only indicators, straws in the wind, but together they would seem to provide a case for asserting that medico-clerical dialogue and co-operation as evidenced in the 1960s and early 1970s is presently in slow but sure decline.[13]

If medico-theological dialogue and clerical-medical co-operation are in fact declining, as has been postulated, it is necessary to move on now to enquire into the future prospects of these activities. This will inevitably be a speculative activity, but, it is to be hoped, an illuminating and helpful one also. It may be that in examining the prospects for medico-religious dialogue and co-operation that it is possible to give some indication as to the reasons for their recent decline. Before proceeding, however, it is useful to put the movement towards dialogue and co-operation in its proper perspective.

Lambourne, in his 1969 paper 'Towards an Understanding of Medico-Theological Dialogue', pointed out that there were considerable dangers and difficulties associated with this activity. In particular he warned that those involved in the dialogue might only represent a tiny minority of their own professional group. It seems likely that this was in fact a trap into which the dialogue and co-operation of the 1960s fell. Those most involved in the movement on both sides tended to be Protestant Christians and intellectual liberals. There is not much sign of doctors who were not Christians or of clergy who were not liberals being involved in the dialogue. The latter assertion can be assayed by referring to the works of Autton, a non-liberal Catholically-inclined Anglican priest, on hospital chaplaincy and pastoral care of the mentally ill.[15] These show that it was perfectly possible even at the height of the movement towards medico-theological dialogue and co-operation, for a cleric to conceptualize his ministry within the health sector in traditional spiritual and sacramental terms.[16] The point under consideration must not be over-estimated. Given the vast numbers of doctors working in the health sector and the lesser number of clergy employed by the churches, the movement towards medico-religious dialogue and co-operation can only be seen as a very tiny minority activity.[17] Let it further be recognized that many of the original points of contact for those involved in the movement have now disappeared or become diminished in importance. In the key area of psychiatry, for example, the concepts provided by psycho-analytic thought and existentialism are no longer such a useful bridging point. The insights of psycho-analysis have been largely rejected by British psychiatrists working in the health service and existentialist thought has diminished in significance in all areas of intellectual life, including that of theology. On a practical level therapeutic communities have run their course and there is a return to more organic, medically-dominated and administered methods of treatment where there is only limited room for lay participation.[18]

What, then, of the future of medico-theological dialogue and co-operation? In fine, the prospects do not look very bright or hopeful. In what follows it will be argued that changes which have and are taking place within the clerical and medical professions are conducive to separation and drifting apart rather than to dialogue and co-operation. In considering this matter the medical profession will be examined first and it will then be the turn of the clergy to be scrutinized.

Until very recently medicine was growing very rapidly in terms of its qualified practitioners.[19] At the same time doctors have continued to become more specialized and highly trained.[20] The medical model of coping with illness by cure rather than prevention, active therapeutic intervention rather than care and specialist attention from qualified experts in the technologically-dominated environment of the hospital has continued to hold sway.[21] While much lip service is paid to the idea of treating the whole person, the reality is that in the dominant acute sector of the health services people are basically treated by doctors as malfunctioning machines.[23] This underlying context gives doctors little incentive to explore the religious dimension of patient care. There is no formal introduction to this area in medical training and so generations of doctors still begin to practice with very limited ideas of the relevance and significance of religion in medicine. This is not a surprising phenomenom in a society which is becoming steadily more secularized, i.e. a society in which organized religion is relinquishing its hold on social beliefs and institutions in the face of ratio-technocratic forms of thought and organizations.[24] Participation in religious belief and activity is becoming a matter for the private individual and it is no longer to be expected that preferential attention should be given to a 'leisure activity' in the secularized health sector. Religious representatives are becoming less important in society as a whole and it is predictable therefore that their diminishing significance will be reflected in the interest of the medical profession, many of whose members may hold no religious convictions at all.[25] Where adherents of many faiths use and work in health care facilities it would appear arbitrary to pay particular attention to Christian clergy. Doctors are under pressure from many directions at this time. Hard-pressed by the Government and its desire to squeeze the public sector, by economists who want to assess value for money in the health sector and thus threaten to interfere with clinical freedom, and by lawyers, philosophers and others who criticize and meddle with medical decision making, it is not surprising that doctors are largely uninterested in becoming involved in dialogue and co-operation with potentially critical voluntary groups whose real capacity to perform good works is apparently vitiated by its unfortunate pre-occupation with abstract metaphysics. Presumably the presence of vast numbers of clergy within the health sector would do much to force the issue on unwilling medical ears, but, it will now be argued in looking at the clerical profession, it is likely that clerical involvement in this area is now declining.

If, during the last twenty years, the medical profession has grown larger, stronger and less likely to enter into dialogue and co-operation with other groups on anything but an *ad hoc* basis because of its commanding position in the health sector the opposite process seems to have occurred within the clerical profession, but with a similar outcome. There are fewer full-time clergy now than there were two decades ago.[27] While numbers of full- and part-time hospital chaplains have remained stable it seems likely that clergy generally, especially those with parishes, now have less time to devote to activities over and above those which have to be performed by ordained persons. Clergy may be choosing, or being forced to fall back on, the narrowly spiritual and sacramental aspects of their role.[28] The element of choice may be important in this connection, for my own impression is that clergy entering full-time ministry are more conservative than their predecessors in the 1960s and therefore they are actively seeking specialism in the traditional aspects of the clerical role. Martin has drawn attention to the advent of the 'therepeutic clergyman' in the midst of rapid social and cultural change at the middle point of the twentieth century. This type of cleric, facing the marginalization of religion and of his own profession, she suggests, eschewed the mystical and prophetic elements of religion in order to become 'a species of semi-professional therapist with a roving brief', a 'generic caseworker for the parish with a mildly spritual aura'. Ethical concern became the hall mark of religious commitment and pastoral care and 'while radical therapists were rediscovering the ancient religious connotation of madness . . . many clergymen were busy demolishing the distinction between the church and the world, and, in so doing, inadvertently abandoning the religious in favour either of secular politics or a mildly therapeutic pastoral role: "only the humane"; no dog collars; no mystery, just good citizenship and informal mateyness.'[29]

The abandoning of this mildly therapeutic pastoral role in favour of the more traditional aspects of priesthood may also have contributed to current interest in distinctively Christian sacramental and spiritual healing methods. While there is a little contemporary thought and writing on religion and medicine amongst liberal Christians, publishing in the area of the Christian healing ministry is in rude good health.[30] Hailed as a recovery of a basic aspect of the Church's ministry, it is difficult not to see the close interest being taken in this movement as part of the drift towards conservatism and sectarianism in theology and practice which stands in antithesis to the liberal mood and thought of two decades ago.

A further, irrevocable phenomenon which has affected the church and its clergy since 1960 is that of de-professionalization. While medical practitioners have become more highly trained, better qualified academically and more specialized, the church has moved in the opposite direction. In many places lay people are taking a much greater part in all aspects of the church's ministry.[31] There are now several different ways of becoming an ordained person and it is possible to be neither paid nor fully employed by the church. Ministry, including pastoral ministry, is becoming lay, variegated and localized. Contrast this with the highly professionalized, specialized and centralized nature of contemporary medicine. Such a fundamental difference of direction in the two professions is almost bound to make inter-professional co-operation and dialogue more complicated. It will no longer be a matter of doctors relating to one, clearly designated, ordained person who has had the benefit of orthodox tertiary education and professional training but to the many different lay and ordained people who are involved in the work of caring rather than curing, centred on the technological wasteland of the community rather than the hospital.[32]

So far, in surveying the clerical aspect of prospects for medico-religious dialogue and co-operation, only factors which are, at least potentially, practical barriers to dialogue and co-operation have been considered. A different aspect must now be considered. The question arises, even if clergy had the time and the inclination to enter into closer relations with doctors is it clear that it is right for them to do so? In the 1960s the dominant view of the medical profession was that it was composed of benevolent technocrats engaged in a vital war against suffering and death. While doctors might do their curing more adequately or take into account more factors than they did in their decisions, there was no fundamental doubting of the value of medicine and of its practitioners. It was possible to regard religion and medicine as allies in a common struggle. Now, however, clergy, in common with other lay people are (or perhaps should be) beginning to have considerable doubts about the wisdom of the alliance and the benevolence and effectiveness of the ally. The assumption that professions with their codes of ethics, qualifications, occupational monopolies and autonomy are the best tools for the alleviation of human need and misery is being closely questioned. In the welfare state as a whole it has been found that policy decisions reflect professional rather than public influences and needs, that services are organized to suit the desires and resources of professional groups rather than the needs of the clientele, that professionals can usurp the place and decisions of planners, managers and politicians in planning, that they tend to bring problems within the bounds of their own concerns, that the needs of particular groups can be ignored by professional workers and that professional decision-making may by-pass important moral and political issues.[33] In the health sector specifically, the predominance, behaviour and usefulness of the medical profession is under critical scrutiny. Illich and others have exposed the phenomenon of 'iatrogenesis', the process whereby doctors may actually cause damage to patients in the course of trying to cure them. These observers have also pointed up the capacity for professionalized health care to disable and make less autonomous those who become the objects of its attentions.[34] Other analysts, particularly in the fields of epidemiology and social medicine, have queried the value and effectiveness of acute medicine and its techniques in the eradication of illness and promotion of health.[35] Sociological investigators, looking at the professional organization of medicine, have pointed up the ways in which features like self-regulation can militate against the best interests of patients in favour of the profession itself.[36] The scientific basis of medical practice and affective neutrality of its practitioners has also been questioned.[37]

Medicine has been arraigned as a covert but effective part of the apparatus of social control in society and some critics claim that more and more social and political issues are being swallowed up by the ever-expanding and ostensibly benevolent empire of medical concern.[38] While it is true that many clergy will have read none of the works cited above their general tenor has become known through the media. Kennedy's 1980 Reith lectures covered much of this ground in a popular form and the attitude of the media generally is becoming much more critical of orthodox medicine and of doctors.[39]

It is no accident that, as the general public's disillusionment with scientific medicine and its professional practitioners grows, there is a parallel growth of interest in alternative medicine.[40] Ranging from religion to herbalism, the approaches found in alternative medical systems find sympathetic and fertile ground amongst Christians and their leaders, themselves heirs to an 'alternative' spiritual and sacramental healing system. Interest in this area may be one of the factors facilitating the present drift of Christians away from dialogue and co-operation with orthodox medicine and its representatives.

Two further contra-indicators must be added to this account of the factors which combine to make an increase in medico-religious dialogue and co-operation unlikely from the clerical standpoint. First, it is being realized that even within the health sector there are other groups of professional workers with whom dialogue and co-operation should, and could perhaps more easily, take place. Doctors are a minority group in the health services and with their abiding pre-occupation with cure they are less obvious partners for dialogue and co-operation than, say, nurses and social workers who tend to have greater interest in care, the area into which Christian ministry fits best. Secondly, clergy have had the disillusioning experience of being dismissed and ignored by doctors for a long time now. Many of those attempting dialogue in the past, with a local GP for example, have found little trust or real interest coming from the other side. While there are clearly outstanding exceptions to this, in general the lesson that clergy are not particularly wanted by doctors in the health sector is being vigorously reinforced all the time. Clergy will not accept such indifference indefinitely and the practical experience of rejection will militate against a general revival of medico-religious dialogue and co-operation.

It has been argued that developments in both the church and medicine over the past few years make a resurgence of medical-clerical co-operation and dialogue unlikely. There is, however, a wider factor which has not been mentioned so far, though it has been hinted at in places. This may be characterized as the 'spirit of the age', an elusive category, to say the least. The decade which saw the burgeoning of medico-religious dialogue and co-operation, the 1960s, may be seen retrospectively as one of idealism and optimism. Great faith was placed in technology and its solutions. The new caring professions like social work were, once fully established, going to make good the ravages of late twentieth-century society on individuals and communities. Poverty and other social problems were (it was believed) being banished for ever in an affluent and expanding economy. A spirit of equality and mutual participation was abroad. Everyone was to receive educational opportunities and health care and, in return, each individual and group was to contribute democratically and equally in a society characterized by consensus. It looked as if liberalism and tolerance had decisively defeated autocracy and elitism in a society where the welfare state bore witness to the firm commitment on the part of all citizens to make society one. The late 1970s and 1980s seem more than an age away from this time. People are once again pessimistic about the future, both for themselves and for their society. Ideals have been replaced by Victorian values. Professionals and technocrats have failed to solve the old problems and appear to have introduced new ones. Poverty and inequality have been 're-discovered' and are once again accepted as permanent features of the social order. Since people are openly regarded as unequal once more there is no attempt now to ask all to contribute to the direction of society on an equal basis. (In the National Health Service line management threatens to overtake consensus management.) Hierarchical organization is back in fashion and the elite are once again invited to exercise overt leadership from the top. The concept of two nations, one rich and one poor, is no longer shocking and the welfare state is regarded as an unnecessary, expensive and debilitating anachronism. The era of liberal consensus in thought and practice has collapsed and given way to overt division and extremism in thought and practice.

If my impressionistic sketch of the 'spirit of the age' is in the smallest part accurate it is not surprising that medico-religious dialogue and co-operation, the product of a union between equality, professionalism, liberalism, tolerance, consensus and optimism, does not flourish today. It may be argued that not until wider society and its values changes can there be any real hope of a revival in this area. It remains to be seen whether medico-theological/clerical-medical co-operation as it occurred from 1960 to the mid-1970s was a brief aberration caused by one or two powerful personalities in a tiny, liberal minority group – or whether it was, in fact, the first fruits of something greater which has yet to come.[41]

Notes

Introduction

1. Stephen Parsons, *The Challenge of Christian Healing*, SPCK 1986.
2. It is John Robinson who, in a completely different context, talks of truth as being 'two-eyed'. See John A. T. Robinson, *Truth is Two-eyed*, SCM Press 1979.
3. Dennis Nineham, *The Use and Abuse of the Bible*, SPCK 1978.
4. For an introduction to the history of medicine and medical historiography see, e.g., Pietro Corsi and Paul Weindling (eds), *Information Sources in the History of Science and Medicine*, Butterworth 1983.
5. For healing see, e.g., Morris Maddocks, *The Christian Healing Ministry*, SPCK 1981, ch. 2; Michael Wilson, *The Church is Healing*, SCM Press 1967; Frank Wright, *The Pastoral Nature of Healing*, SCM Press 1985, ch. 2; for health see, e.g., David Seedhouse, *Health: The Foundations for Achievement*, John Wiley 1986, Michael Wilson, *Health is for People*, Darton, Longman and Todd 1975. Healing and illness are, unfortunately, concepts which chase after meaning.

1. Towards a Fundamental Practical Theology of Illness and Healing

1. Michael Wilson, *The Church is Healing*, SCM Press 1967.
2. See, e.g., Morris Maddocks, *The Christian Healing Ministry*, SPCK 1981. For works by Lambourne see R. A. Lambourne, *Community, Church and Healing*, Darton, Longman and Todd 1963, Michael Wilson (ed.), *Explorations in Health and Salvation*, University of Birmingham Institute for the Study of Worship and Religious Architecture 1983. For Wilson's work see, e.g., Michael Wilson, op. cit.; *The Hospital: A Place of Truth*, University of Birmingham Institute for the Study of Worship and Religious Architecture, 1971; *Health is for People*, Darton, Longman and Todd 1975.
3. The notion of 'fundamental practical theology' may be obscure or unfamiliar. I draw the concept from the work of the American pastoral theologian, Don Browning. Browning strongly advocates the formulation of contemporary normative and action-guiding theologies which focus round practical issues and within which Christian thinking and action can be situated. These theologies are constructed on the basis of careful rational, critical and public dialogue between interpretations of the Christian theological tradition

and contemporary sources of knowledge and information about particular phenomena or situations. See further Don S. Browning, *Religious Ethics and Pastoral Care*, Philadelphia: Fortress Press 1983; Browning (ed.), *Practical Theology* San Francisco: Harper and Row 1983.

4. See further, e.g., Colin Brown, *That You May Believe*, Eerdmans/Paternoster 1985, Rex Gardner, *Healing Miracles*, Darton, Longman and Todd 1986; David E. Jenkins, *God, Miracle and the Church of England*, SCM Press 1988; Ernst and Marie Keller, *Miracles in Dispute*, SCM Press 1969; M. A. H. Melinsky, *Healing Miracles*, Mowbray 1968; C. F. D. Moule, *Miracles*, Mowbray 1965; Richard Swinburne, *The Concept of Miracle*, Macmillan 1970.

5. See further, e.g., Andrew Stanway, *Alternative Medicine*, Penguin 1979; Anne Oakley, *The Captured Womb*, Blackwell 1984.

6. See, e.g., Gary Easthope, *Healers and Alternative Medicine*, Gower 1986; Ted Kaptchuk and Michael Croucher, *The Healing Arts*, BBC 1986; Francis MacNutt, *Healing*, Notre Dame: Ave Maria Press 1974; Stephen Parsons, *The Challenge of Christian Healing*, SPCK, 1986; John Wimber, *Power Healing*, Hodder and Stoughton, 1986. There are also autobiographical accounts by those who have been healed. See, e.g., Frances Parsons, *Pools of Water*, Triangle, 1987.

7. For a introduction to different levels and types of health knowledge in society see Cecil Helman, *Culture, Health and Illness*, Wright 1985.

8. The social psychology of attribution of explanations is illuminating in considering this area. See further, e.g., Miles Hewstone (ed.), *Attribution Theory*, Blackwell 1983; C. R. Snyder, Raymond L. Higgins and Rita J. Stucky, *Excuses*, John Wiley 1983. Many works bearing on the social history of medicine illustrate very effectively the way in which different belief and knowledge systems can exist alongside each other and also point up the way in which 'lay' knowledge can differ radically from and lag behind professional knowledge and explanations. See further, e.g., Keith Thomas, *Religion and the Decline of Magic*, Penguin 1973; Christina Larner, *Witchcraft and Religion*, Blackwell 1984; Lucinda McCray Beier, *Sufferers and Healers*, Routledge and Kegan Paul 1987; and, especially, Roy Porter, (ed.), *Patients and Practitioners*, Cambridge University Press 1985.

9. In a recent book on pastoral care with ill people Peter Speck, for example, seems to find no illumination at all in the theological tradition for looking at illness and healing. See Peter Speck, *Being There*, SPCK 1988.

10. Contemporary liberal theologians have been undertaking a fundamental reconstruction of the ways in which we think about the nature and character of God, the nature of divine intervention and causation in the world and of the nature of evil and suffering. Their thought has far-reaching but hitherto ignored implications for the whole area of healing and illness. See further, e.g., Langdon Gilkey, 'God', in Peter Hodgson and Robert King (eds.), *Christian Theology*, SPCK, 1983; Jim Garrison, *The Darkness of God*, SCM Press 1982; Gordon Kaufman, *Theology for a Nuclear Age*, Manchester

University Press 1985; Sallie McFague, *Models of God*, SCM Press 1987; Ken Surin, *Theology and the Problem of Evil*, Blackwell 1986.

11. The following works all bear on the significance of Jesus' healing ministry directly or indirectly: Howard C. Kee, *Miracle in the Early Christian-World*, Yale University Press 1983; *Medicine, Miracle and Magic in New Testament Times*, Cambridge University Press 1986; Albert Nolan, *Jesus Before Christianity*, Darton, Longman and Todd 1977; E. P. Sanders, *Jesus and Judaism*, SCM Press 1985; Morton Smith, *Jesus the Magician*, Aquarian, 1985; Gerd Theissen, *Sociology of Early Palestinian Christianity*, Philadelphia: Foretress Press 1978; *The Shadow of the Galilean*, SCM Press 1987; Geza Vermes, *Jesus the Jew*, Collins 1976; rev. ed. SCM Press 1983. All these books, needless to say, offer very different perspectives on the healing ministry of Jesus. Their cumulative effect, however, is to create problems for the idea that Jesus was a good, kind man who performed 'real' cures out of a sense of compassion for individuals. In particular, the influence of the early church on the interpretation of Jesus' healings is pointed up and the healing ministry comes to look much more like part of a publicity campaign aimed at attracting mass attention for a message rather than a quest for the personal well-being of particular individuals. If these interpretations are anything like correct, they have significant implications for Christian perspective on healing and illness today. Simple imitation of Jesus becomes impossible while culture and context become crucial for appropriate healing responses. For works on hermeneutics and interpretation see, e.g., Robert M. Grant and David Tracey, *A Short History of the Interpretation of the Bible*, SCM Press 1984; Anthony C. Thiselton, *The Two Horizons*, Paternoster 1980.

12. See J. G. Davies, *Liturgical Dance*, SCM Press 1984 and James B. Nelson, *Embodiment*, SPCK 1979 for more on Christian attitudes to the body over the centuries. A thorough history of these attitudes and attitudes to illness and healing still needs to be written.

13. Throughout the history of Western civilization there has been a strong association between moral and physical sanitation. It is not for nothing that sin, physical defilement and disease have been so closely linked. See further, e.g., Mary Douglas, *Purity and Danger*, Routledge and Kegan Paul 1970; *Natural Symbols*, Penguin 1973. For examples of this association in action see, e.g., Anne G. Carmichael, *Plague and the Poor in Renaissance Florence*, Cambridge University Press 1986, pp. 96ff.; Geoffrey Pearson, *The Deviant Imagination*, Macmillan 1975, especially ch. 6.

14. See, e.g., Bryan S. Turner, *The Body and Society*, Blackwell 1984; *Medical Knowledge and Social Power*, Sage 1987. See also David Armstrong, *Political Anatomy of the Body*, Cambridge University Press 1983; Catherine Gallagher and Thomas Lacquer, (eds.), *The Making of the Modern Body*, Berkeley: University of California Press 1987; two historical studies on the intellectual construction of the body. Elaine Scarry, *The Body in Pain*, Oxford University Press 1985, examines the vocabularies used to describe and construct the body.

15. See below pp. 26ff. for further consideration of this evidence.

16. See the work of R. A. Lambourne cited in n. 2 above. Lambourne always emphasizes the social and corporate context of illness and healing.

17. The last serious study of the National Health Service sponsored by a Christian body to my knowledge is Tom Heller, *Restructuring the Health Service*, Croom Helm 1978. This study was sponsored by the William Temple Foundation. It has no element of overt theological critique in it.

18. See, however, Jerome D. Frank, *Persuasion and Healing*, New York: Shocken 1974; Edgar N. Jackson, *The Role of Faith in the Process of Healing*, SCM Press 1981; Stephen Parsons, *The Challenge of Christian Healing*, SPCK 1986, especially chs 7 and 8.

19. For expositions of the importance of the ministry of deliverance see, e.g., Philip Pare, *God Made the Devil?*, Darton Longman and Todd 1985; Michael Perry (ed.), *Deliverance*, SPCK 1987; John Richards, *But Deliver Us From Evil*, Darton, Longman and Todd 1974.

20. In his four-volume historical study of the Devil, Russell argues that personifications of Satan may indeed be metaphors, but that this is not in itself a reason for suggesting that the experience of evil is not real in the modern world: 'Moral relativism is fashionable in many circles today, but more profess to believe in it than actually behave as if they did. If good and evil do not exist, then one has no grounds on which to complain about anything, nothing real to hope for, and one's own ideas and values are arbitrary and artificial and need to be taken seriously by no one. Few practice such a faith.' (Jeffrey B. Russell, *Lucifer*, Ithaca: Cornell University Press 1984, p. 302). See also Jeffrey B. Russell, *The Devil* (1977), *Satan* (1981), *Mephistopheles* (1986), all published by Cornell University Press. Other writers also provide valuable background for consideration of evil, exorcism, possession and the Devil today. A careful reading of some of the following works might do much to modify the tranquil re-demonization of the world by writers such as those cited in n. 19 above. See, e.g., Subniv Babuta and Jean Claude Bragard, *Evil*, Weidenfield and Nicolson 1988; Jim Garrison, op. cit.; I. M. Lewis, *Ecstatic Religion*, Penguin 1971; *Religion in Context*, Cambridge University Press 1986; David Parker (ed.), *The Anthropology of Evil*, Blackwell 1986; John A. Sanford, *Evil*, New York: Crossroad 1987; Kenneth Surin, op. cit.

A particularly illuminating book is D. P. Walker, *Unclean Spirits*, Scolar 1981, a study of possession and exorcism in the late sixteenth and early seventeenth centuries in France and England. This work, amongst the others mentioned, has done much to convince me that the 'possessed' or 'obsessed' are often taught how to behave by their exorcists as well as by the media and they then 'perform' according to type (cf. Thomas J. Scheff, *Being Mentally Ill*, Chicago: Aldine 1966 for instructive parallels here). Often they convincingly vindicate the power and beliefs of those who seek to exorcise them. Strangely, evil spirits who obsess individuals seem rather petty in their behaviour. Their wicked antics are dwarfed by the global evils which we presently suffer and which are not attributed to the Devil or spirits but should rather be seen as human responsibilities, e.g., famine, the arms race. The evangelical psychiatrist, M. J. Barker, also fights shy of the attribution of demon possession, seeing it as often being a way of externalizing problems rather than dealing with them in disturbed people (M. J. Barker, 'Possession and the occult – a psychiatrist's view', *Churchman*, 94, 1980, 3, pp. 246–53). There can be no doubt that evil is real and should be dealt with in the modern world; personalizing and individualizing it may, however, distract humans from taking real responsibility for the ills of the world: 'The Satan image, even where it lingers on, has been whittled down to the stature of a personal being whose sole obsessions would seem to be with adolescent promiscuity, adolescent rebellion, crime, passion and greed. While not in themselves trivial, these preoccupations altogether obscure the massive Satanic evils that plunge and drive our times like a trawler before an angry sea' (Walter Wink, *Unmasking the Powers*, Philadelphia: Fortress Press 1986, p. 9).

The most vivid example of the trivilization of evil and of the way in which so-called 'evil spirits' may be more a product of social learning and pressure is to be found in Richards, op. cit. Richards recounts an incident in which he was visiting a home of healing where deliverance ministry was practised. He was surprised to find that a young possessed man could be tranquil and still. On enquiry, he was told that, 'at the end of a period of ministry that day, the demons had been *bound* until he was due for another session. In fact, I later learnt that in such a community where a number of people had trouble of this nature, the Community simply could not function if emergency prayer-sessions were happening all the time. There was a time set each day for "ministry" as they termed it, and anyone causing any disturbance was "bound" until an appropriate time.' (Richards, op. cit., p. 170, emphasis original.) The significance of this account for me is that the possessed, like shamans in trances, are acutely aware of social norms and boundaries and know quite well when not to manifest their more spectacular symptoms. This behaviour is in every way analogous with that of psychiatric patients who are able to modify their behaviour to some extent in order to attain by informal means desired ends; so they may manifest more symptoms to gain hospital admission, or less if they wish to be transferred to a better ward. On demon possession in general, then, one is tempted to agree with the doctors who examined the case of the demoniac Marthe Brossier in sixteenth-century France and concluded that there was 'nothing from the devil, much counter-feited, a little from disease'. (Walker, op. cit., p. 35.)

I do not want to deny the subjective convictions of the possessed and those who exorcise them in modern society; there is room for many views of disease and disorder – who is to say what is real or what is not real? I do, however, want to point up the limitations and possible dangers into which Richards and his fellows are prone to fall. Although Richards' book has the appearance of being scholarly and well-weighed (it is often cited as a classic and authoritative work), the evidence upon which it rests come mainly from exorcists and others directly concerned with the ministry of deliverance themselves. When medical sources are cited in the text, they are usually very dated. When authors like social anthropologist I. M. Lewis are cited they are only used to corroborate the reality of the existence of possession, not to question the objectivity of such phenomena. Lewis himself makes no claims about the 'reality' of evil spirits and constantly emphasizes the social context, ritualized roles and secondary social benefits associated with possession (cf. Lewis, *Ecstatic Religion*). Richards is correct in his assertions that demons are very real in the Bible and that we are told very little about their nature. But his own contention that the ministry of deliverance should be situated within a larger theological horizon would seem to demand that he provide something more in the way of explanation as to what demons are and what part they play in the divine providence, as well as what is to be made of them in the sophisticated urban cultural context of the twentieth century. The omission of this kind of discussion and explanation (which is endemic in all deliverance literature) delivers his practical advice about deliverance into the hands of pragmatists, sensationalists and those who hold magical and dualistic world views. Ultimately, the book helps to make a very dubious demonization of people and of the world respectable. Despite very sound theological principles such as realism, attending to the good and creative work of God rather than becoming fascinated by evil, and attending to the present, in practice Richards actually helps to create the occult world view which he criticizes so effectively and strongly.

It is certainly true that many of us experience evil and forces beyond our control and ken from time to time, but surely there is a responsibility to try and understand these things in a relatively sophisticated way, rather than uncritically adopting the methods of the first few Christian centuries and a very different cultural context. It is a sobering thought that there are probably more exorcisms occurring today than there have been for the last fifteen hundred years – this is a time when we have never had so much access to effective medical and psychological cures. It may be that deliverance helps some people; there is some evidence that on occasion it harms people. Whatever the therapeutic benefits for particular individuals, the question needs to be asked, 'Is it really going to help if the world and individual experience are re-demonized so that causes of malaise are believed to come from outside human hearts?' This question achieves enormous practical significance when it is remembered that homosexual people and other 'deviants' can often be seen as demon-possessed. It is only a short step from seeing people as demon-possessed to seeing them as demons themselves and so excluding them from society or even destroying them. This is what happened to those regarded as witches in the sixteenth and seventeenth centuries (see further, e.g., Christina Larner, *Enemies of God*, Blackwell 1983).

Before the ministry of deliverance attains wider acceptance in the religious community, it needs to do more to develop its theological rationale and to show that any benefits which might be gained will outweigh disadvantages for individuals and society as a whole in terms of demonization. Until this happens, those who devour the ideas of Richards and his like should perhaps eat with a long spoon! None of this, however, should detract from the enormous importance of assessing and combatting evil at all levels in the world. We badly need new theologies and stategies for dealing with the realities of evil, particularly at the corporate and social levels.

21. From a non-theistic position, Mary Midgley argues that evil has no positive personal existence, but that in the same way as cold can be felt as a reality, wickedness has a reality when a single (good) aspect of personality or concern is pursued to the exclusion of other aspects. See Mary Midgley, *Wickedness*, Routledge and Kegan Paul 1986. This concept is deeply suggestive for understanding why good ideas and practices seem to have an enormous capacity for going wrong and spawning evil. Thus doctors obsessed with the single good of learning how to perform liver transplants may wreak considerable evil upon their own patients, in so far as they see them only as experimental material, not as people with emotional needs, or upon the National Health Service as a whole, in so far as they make large demands for cash which may have to be taken from other sections of the NHS or because they raise public expectations and demand for expensive health care. Such obsession can, of course, be harmful to an individual physician or scientist him-or herself in so far as they fail to develop all aspects of their personality and existence.

22. Walter Wink's work on the heavenly powers in the New Testament is very relevant here. Wink suggests that the spiritual powers in the New Testament are the determining forces of physical, social and psychic life. All of these powers have both a physical manifestation and an inner spiritual manifestation. They are incarnate in social institutions, but they also have an inner nature. Thus the spirit of a church community is invisible and interior on one level but it is also manifest in a building and the structure of a concrete group of people. Such spirits or powers can serve God or turn away from him. This way of seeing social institutions as having an inner and outer reality which has potential for good or evil is suggestive for Christian approaches to major institutions in our own society, such as the National Health Service. See further, Walter Wink, *Naming the Powers*, Philadelphia: Fortress Press 1984; *Unmasking the Powers*, Philadelphia: Fortress Press 1986; *Encountering the Powers*, Philadelphia: Fortress Press, forthcoming.

23. Surin, op. cit., is an important pointer here.

24. See, e.g., M. A. Screech, 'Good Madness', in W. F. Bynum, Roy Porter and Michael Shepherd (eds), *The Anatomy of Madness*, Tavistock 1985. Also see below, ch. 5, for further discussion of this.

25. See, e.g. the order for the Visitation of the sick in the Church of England's *Book of Common Prayer*.

26. See further, e.g., Ivan Illich, *Limits to Medicine*, Marion Boyars 1976; Ivan Illich et al., *Disabling Professions*, Marion Boyars 1977.

27. The importance of confidence on the part of the healing practitioner

evoking reciprocal trust and faith in the person seeking healing is emphasized in Easthope, op. cit.

28. The whole area of conflict in illness and healing is discussed in detail in ch. 4 below. Appropriate references are given there.

29. This discussion is further developed in ch. 4.

30. For more on the moral horizons of our knowledge of the world and the metaphors we live by, see Browning, *Religious Ethics and Pastoral Care* and Don S. Browning, *Religious Thought and the Modern Psychologies*, Philadelphia: Fortress Press 1987; Don Cupitt, *The New Christian Ethics*, SCM Press 1988.

2. Perspectives on Illness

1. Two books provide an overall view of the different possible perspectives on illness and healing. These are Arthur L. Caplan, H. Tristram Engelhardt and James McCartney (eds), *Concepts of Health and Disease*, Reading, Mass: Addison Wesley 1981; Caroline Currer and Margaret Stacey (eds), *Concepts of Health, Illness and Disease*, Berg 1986. Course books for the Open University course, 'Health and Disease', also provide an excellent and easily accessible introduction to this area. see, e.g., Nick Black, David Boswell, Alastair Gray, Sean Murphy and Jennie Popay (eds), *Health and Disease: A Reader*, Open University Press 1984. A brief but very useful book introducing this whole area is Glin Bennet, *Patients and their Doctors*, Balliere Tindall 1979.

2. George L. Engel, 'The Need for the New Medical Model: A Challenge for Biomedicine', in Caplan et al. (eds), op. cit.

3. F. F. Cartwright, *A Social History of Medicine*, Longman 1977, provides a short, readable, simplistic and triumphalistic Whig account of biomedical 'progress'. More complex, critical and detailed accounts of the history of modern medicine are to be found in, e.g., Erwin H. Ackerknecht, *A Short History of Medicine*, Johns Hopkins University Press 1982; Roy Porter, *Disease, Medicine and Society in England 1550–1860*, Macmillan 1987; Richard Shryock, *The Development of Modern Medicine*, University of Wisconsin Press 1979. Porter and Shryock in particular show up the social context of medical development which makes it less clear that there has been simple linear 'progress'.

4. See Lawrie Reznek, *The Nature of Disease*, Routledge and Kegan Paul 1987. Lester S. King, *Medical Thinking*, Princeton University Press 1982, also provides historical background to the evolution of the modern disease concept. Many articles in Caplan et al. (eds), op. cit., relate to this topic.

5. For further critical material on the disease model from a theological perspective see Michael Wilson, *Health is for People*, Darton, Longman and Todd 1975; Wilson (ed.), *Explorations in Health and Salvation*, University of Birmingham Institute for the Study of Worship and Religious Architecture 1983.

6. The relationship between body and mind is, of course, a reciprocal one.

Physical well-being also affects mental state, hence there are somatopsychic conditions as well as psychosomatic ones.

7. See Bennet, op. cit., pp. 11–12.

8. See Peter Lambley, *The Psychology of Cancer*, Futura 1987, ch. 2.

9. See Bennet, op. cit., ch. 2. Bennet cites studies of increased incidence of morbidity and mortality when, for example, a hospital closes or people lose their homes due to flooding.

10. For an introduction to behavioural psychology see, e.g., Leonard Kristal, *Understanding Psychology*, Harper and Row 1979.

11. The philosophy that people are basically responsible for their own illness and health underlies much contemporary governmental thinking. See further, e.g., DHSS, *Prevention and Health: Everybody's Business*, HMSO 1976. For the critique of this tendency see, e.g., Lesley Doyal, *The Political Economy of Health*, Pluto Press 1979, ch. 1; Wendy Farrant and Jill Russell, *The Politics of Health Information*, University of London Institute of Education 1986.

12. See further, e.g., Margaret Pelling, *Cholera, Fever and English Medicine 1825–1865*, Oxford University Press 1978; Derek Frazer, *The Evolution of the British Welfare State*, Macmillan 1973, ch. 3.

13. Thomas McKeown, *The Role of Medicine*, Blackwell 1979. McKeown's analysis has been challenged. See, e.g., Simon Szreter, 'The importance of social intervention in Britain's mortality decline c. 1850–1914: a re-interpretation of the role of public health', *Social History of Medicine 1*, 1988, 1–38.

14. Peter Townsend and Nick Davidson (eds), *Inequalities in Health*, Penguin 1988.

15. Ibid., pp. 55–6.

16. Margaret Whitehead, *The Health Divide*, in Townsend and Davidson (eds), op. cit.

17. See James McCormick, *The Doctor: Father Figure or Plumber?*, Croom Helm 1979 for this distinction.

18. Further discussions and outlines of this topic can be sought in, e.g., David Field, 'The Social Definition of Illness' in David Tuckett (ed.), *An Introduction to Medical Sociology*, Tavistock 1976, David Mechanic, *Medical Sociology*, New York: Free Press 1978, chs 1, 2, and 3, Joel Richman, *Medicine and Health*, Longman 1987, ch. 3.

19. A role in this connection is a set of social expectations.

20. A fictional example which points up the relativity of illness attribution is Samuel Butler, *Erewhon*, Penguin 1970. In this novel, colds and other infections are regarded as culpable and sufferers are punished, while those who commit crimes receive comfort, care and commiseration.

21. See further, e.g., R. Littlewood and M. Lipsedge, *Aliens and Alienists*, Penguin 1982.

22. See further, e.g., Peter Conrad and Joseph W. Schneider, *Deviance and Medicalisation*, St Louis: Mosby 1980; Barbara and John Ehrenreich,

'Medicine and Social Control' and Irving K. Zola, 'Medicine as an Institution of Social Control' in John W. Ehrenreich (ed.), *The Cultural Crisis of Modern Medicine*, New York: Monthly Review Press 1978. Zola asserts, '. . . medicine is becoming a major institution of social control, nudging aside, if not incorporating, the more traditional institutions of religion and the law. It is becoming the new repository of truth, the place where absolute and often final judgments are made by supposedly morally neutral and objective experts. And these judgments are made, not in the name of virtue or legitimacy, but in the name of health.' (Zola, op. cit., p. 80.)

23. For a good discussion of the advantages and disadvantages of a condition being designated a sickness see Conrad and Schneider, op. cit., ch. 1.

24. For a full discussion of this see Mechanic, op. cit., ch. 9.

25. Cf. Eliot Freidson, *Professional Dominance*, Chicago: Aldine Press 1970; *Profession of Medicine*, New York: Dodd, Mead 1975.

26. David Robinson, *Patients, Practitioners and Medical Care*, Heinemann 1978, pp. 62–3.

27. For more on the doctor-patient relationship and appropriate references, see below pp. 96f.

28. There are several collections which contain medical anthropological material, e.g., Caplan et al. (eds), op. cit.; Currer and Stacey (eds), op. cit.; J. B. Loudon (ed.), *Social Anthropology and Medicine*, Academic Press 1976. By far the most accessible and easily obtainable introduction to the area is Cecil Helman, *Culture, Health and Illness*, Wright 1984. See also Horatio Fabrega, *Disease and Social Behavior*, Massachussets Institute of Technology Press 1980; Arthur Kleinman, *Patients and Healers in the Context of Culture*, University of California Press 1980. In Littlewood and Lipsedge, op. cit., an anthropological approach is adopted in looking at mental disorder amongst ethnic minorities.

29. Helman, op. cit., p. 2.

30. Ibid., p. 1.

31. See further, e.g., Una Maclean, *Magical Medicine*, Penguin 1974; Aylward Shorter, *Jesus and the Witchdoctor*, Geoffrey Chapman 1985.

32. Cecil Helman, ' "Feed a Cold, Starve a Fever": Folk Models of Infection in an English Suburban Community, and their Relation to Medical Treatment' in Currer and Stacey (eds), op. cit., pp. 221–2. This article can also be found in Black et al. (eds), op. cit.

33. See further Claudine Herzlich and Janine Pierret, 'Illness: From Causes to Meaning' in Currer and Stacey (eds), op. cit.

34. Alan Kleinman, 'Concepts and a Model for the Comparison of Medical Systems and Cultural Systems' in Currer and Stacey (eds), op. cit.

35. See Jocelyn Cornwell, *Hard Earned Lives*, Tavistock 1984, for this example.

36. See further, e.g., George Lakoff and Mark Johnson, *Metaphors We Live By*, University of Chicago Press 1980.

37. This perception is well expressed by the theologian Sallie McFague in

a different context: 'I agree with the deconstructionists that all constructions are metaphorical and hence miss the mark. . . . To claim that all constructions are metaphorical is to insist that one never experiences reality "raw"; it does not follow from this, however, that there is nothing outside language. All that follows is that our access to reality is in every case mediated and hence partial and relative.' (Sallie McFague, *Models of God*, SCM Press 1987, p. 26).

38. David Armstrong, *Political Anatomy of the Body*, Cambridge University Press 1983. Compare Michel Foucault, *The Birth of the Clinic*, Tavistock 1973. The latter is a consideration of 'the archaeology of medical perception'. Articles in Peter Wright and Andrew Treacher, *The Problem of Medical Knowledge*, Edinburgh University Press 1982, also bear upon this subject matter.

39. See Charles Singer, *A Short History of Anatomy and Physiology from the Greeks to Harvey*, New York: Dover 1957, p. 43.

40. See Londa Schiebinger, 'Skeletons in the Closet: Illustrations of the Female Skeleton in Eighteenth-Century Anatomy' in Catherine Gallagher and Thomas Laqueur (eds), *The Making of the Modern Body*, University of California Press 1987.

41. Quoted in Armstrong, op. cit., p. 1.

42. Ibid., pp. 1–2.

43. Ibid., p. 2. Further material relating to radically changing perceptions of the body and bodily disorder is to be found in Bryan S. Turner, *The Body and Society*, Blackwell 1984; Stanley J. Reiser, *Medicine and the Reign of Technology*, Cambridge University Press 1978.

44. Susan Sontag, *Illness as Metaphor*, New York: Vintage 1979.

45. See further, e.g., Allan Brandt, *No Magic Bullet*, Oxford University Press 1987; Simon Watney, *Policing Desire*, Comedia 1987.

46. See further ch. 6 below, also Watney, op. cit. Watney remarks sharply about one medical reporter, 'Nor has she registered the fact that monogamy is no more of an immediate protection from Aids than is prayer, or fasting. Aids is not contracted by promiscuity, but by blood, which is common even to moral paragons such as Ms Chapman.' (Watney, op. cit., p. 119.)

47. For this account here, I draw mainly on Ilza Veith, 'Historical Reflections on Changing Concepts of Disease' in Caplan et al., op. cit. But see also reference in n. 3 above.

48. Keith Thomas, *Religion and the Decline of Magic*, Penguin 1973.

49. See, e.g., McKeown, op. cit., A. L. Cochrane, *Effectiveness and Efficiency*, Nuffield Provincial Hospitals Trust 1971; Brian Inglis, *The Diseases of Civilisation*, Granada 1981; Ian Kennedy, *The Unmasking of Medicine*, George Allen and Unwin 1981. See also Appendix B, pp. 148ff.

50. See King, op. cit.; Reznek, op. cit.

51. See John Bowker, *Licensed Insanities*, Darton, Longman and Todd 1987, pp. 100ff., for a discussion of constraints and causes.

52. This distinction is made in relation to the explanations offered by working class women for illness in Cornwell, op. cit.

53. For a summary of this evidence, its interpretation and significance, see, e.g., Jennifer King, 'Attribution Theory and the Health Belief Model' in Miles Hewstone (ed.), *Attribution Theory*, Blackwell 1983. Gurnek Bains, 'Explanations and the Need for Control' in Hewstone (ed.), op. cit.; Melvin J. Lerner, *The Belief in a Just World*, New York: Plenum 1980, and C. R. Snyder, Raymond L. Higgins, Anita J. Stucky, *Excuses*, New York: John Wiley 1983 are also relevant to understanding the use and function of explanation psychologically. A philosophical introduction to explanation can be found in Daniel M. Taylor, *Explanation and Meaning*, Cambridge University Press 1970.

54. At this point readers may find it helpful to refer to Appendix A which is a diagrammatic representation of the relationships and tensions between the different perspectives provided in this chapter. The diagram was formulated by Janet Mayer. I am very grateful to her for it.

3. Contemporary Christian Responses to Illness and Healing

1. Morton Kelsey, *Healing and Christianity*, SCM Press 1973.

2. A modern defence of this view can be found in Michael Wilson, *The Church is Healing*, SCM Press 1967.

3. The correlation between sin and sickness is ambivalent in its effects. On the one hand, it seems to promote a very dubious view of a loving God, but on the other, it actually allows people to find reason and meaning in their misfortune, a very important thing in itself (See further ch. 2, n. 53 above). Biomedicine prescinds from finding meaning in illness and simply seeks to eliminate it. This has been criticized by theologians like Wilson and Speck (see, e.g. Peter Speck, *Being There*, SPCK 1988; Michael Wilson, *Health is for People*, Darton Longman and Todd 1975). But once the quest for finding meaning in illness has been embarked upon, it is all too easy to end up reviving direct causal connections between sin and sickness. Hence the putative correlation in the minds of some Christians between homosexual relationships and contracting AIDS (see further ch. 6 below). What is required here, then, is a much closer analysis of the use of explanation in illness. Does believing that illness is due to sin actually make a person feel better? Does it serve real present needs for meaning and thus for control? On this topic see pp. 41f. above.

4. A defence of this view is contained in Colin Brown, *That You May Believe*, Eerdmans/Paternoster 1985.

5. See Kelsey, op. cit., ch. 2.

6. Kelsey's interpretation is broadly supported by the historical survey material in Martin E. Marty and Kenneth L. Vaux, *Health/Medicine and the Faith Traditions*, Philadelphia: Fortress Press 1982.

7. See futher, e.g., Peter Brown, *The Cult of the Saints*, SCM Press 1981; Ronald C. Finucane, *Miracles and Pilgrims*, Dent 1977; Patrick Marnham, *Lourdes*, Heinemann 1980; Victor Turner and Edith Turner, *Image and Pilgrimage in Christian Culture*, Blackwell 1978.

8. See Judith F. Champ, 'Bishop Milner, Holywell and the Cure Tradition' in W. J. Sheils (ed.), *The Church and Healing*, Blackwell 1982.

9. Keith Thomas, *Religion and the Decline of Magic*, Penguin 1973.

10. This characterization of the purpose of God and the church is drawn from Paul Lehmann, *Ethics in a Christian Context*, New York: Harper and Row 1963.

11. John Bowden, *Jesus: The Unanswered Questions*, SCM Press 1988, poses the problem of Christian pluralism in practice and belief in a sharp and fundamental way.

12. John Richards (ed.), *The Church's Healing Ministry*, Marshall Pickering 1983.

13. The beginnings of such evaluation can, however, be found in, e.g. Gary Easthope, *Healers and Alternative Medicine*, Gower 1986 (a sociological study); Walter J. Hollenweger, *The Pentecostals*, SCM Press 1972 (a social and theological study); Morton Kelsey, op. cit. (a historical and theological study); David C. Lewis, 'Signs and Wonders in Sheffield: A Social Anthropologist's Analysis of Words of Knowledge and the Effectiveness of Divine Healing' in John Wimber, *Power Healing*, Hodder and Stoughton 1986; Morris Maddocks, *Christian Healing Ministry*, SPCK 1981; Marty and Vaux, op. cit. (historical and ethical studies); Stuart Mews, 'The Revival of Spiritual Healing in the Church of England' in W J Sheils (ed.), *The Church and Healing*, Blackwell 1982 (a historical study); Stephen Parsons, *The Challenge of Christian Healing*, SPCK 1986 (a survey and theological evaluation); John Richards, 'The Church's Healing Ministry and the Charismatic Renewal' in David Martin and Peter Mullen (eds), *Strange Gifts?*, Blackwell 1984 (a theological and historical study).

14. See further, e.g., Thomas McKeown, *The Role of Medicine*, Blackwell 1979; F. B. Smith, *The People's Health*, Croom Helm 1979.

15. Fuller outlines of this history can be found in Maddocks, op. cit.; Mews, op. cit.; Richards, op. cit. None of these is exhaustive or definitive, however.

16. See, e.g., Maddocks, op. cit.; Christopher Hamel Cooke, *Health is for God*, Arthur James 1986.

17. See futher Hollenweger, op. cit.

18. There has been a tension between healing as an individual charismatic gift as against healing as a corporate act of the church and its ministry since New Testament times. Compare I Cor. 12.28ff. and James 5. 14ff.

19. See Mews, op. cit.

20. Established churches have been under pressure from the charismatic movement in many different areas. Arguably, the move towards establishing small groups in parish churches is at least partly a response to the intimacy and enthusiasm of house churches.

21. The Institute of Religion and Medicine was formed after the publication of a report by an Archbishops' Commission, *The Church's Ministry of Healing*, Church Information Board 1958. The report was compiled by leading clergy,

doctors and others. On the whole, it took a very dim view of charismatic or spiritual healing. Healing was generally best left to health care professionals. This was in line with the attitude adopted by liberal intellectual church leaders who throughout the present century have tended to the view that the age of miracles is over, even if healing remains very important. The latest and most vociferous exponent of this attitude is Henson's successor at Durham, David Jenkins. See, e.g., David Jenkins, *God, Miracle and the Church of England*, SCM Press 1988.

22. Parsons, op. cit., ch. 2 points out that many charismatic healers work on the fringes of the mainstream churches and often feel marginalized or unacceptable within them.

23. Herbert Hensley Henson, *Notes on Spiritual Healing*, Williams and Norbury 1925, is a scurrilous and vitriolic attack on religious healing methods as practised by Hickson and others. Interestingly, it also attacks the nascent psychoanalytic movement which was closely associated with the spiritual healing movement at that time.

24. See further Appendix B below.

25. For an overview of the various different Christian healing practices available see e.g., Easthope, op. cit., ch. 3; Parsons, op. cit.

26. See further David E. Harrell, *All Things are Possible*, Indiana University Press 1975.

27. The healers Parsons descibes in op. cit. seem to come, by and large, from humble social origins. The same seems to be true of Harrell's healers in the US (see Harrell, op. cit.). In this connection, gaining healing abilities seems to be a way of obtaining power and significance for those who are relatively poor and who are marginalized in terms of access to educational and professional opportunities. A classic pattern appears to be that a person from a deprived background falls ill, has a personal experience of being healed and then starts to heal others (this is very reminiscent of the way shamans start to heal in traditional societies – see further, e.g., I. M. Lewis, *Ecstatic Religion*, Penguin 1971). After healing intensively for a few years, they graduate more to evangelism and build up large and expensive evangelistic organizations. This pattern, interestingly, is shown to some extent in the career of the Irish Catholic nun, Sister Briege McKenna. Starting from very humble origins as a nobody in a male-dominated, hierarchical church, Sr Briege had an experience of illness and healing which led her into healing others. She is now the adviser of priests, cardinals and even the Pope. See Briege McKenna, *Miracles do Happen*, Pan 1987, especially ch. 2 where she describes being healed and called.

28. Francis MacNutt, *Healing*, Notre Dame: Ave Maria Press 1974.

29. This is discussed further in Parsons, op. cit., ch. 2. The divide reflects a basic theological difference between those who see the Spirit of God as acting in the whole of creation and those who want to situate it primarily within the realm of Christian redemption only. See further W. J. Hollenweger, 'All

Creatures Great and Small: Towards a Pneumatology of Life' in David Martin and Peter Mullen (eds), *Strange Gifts?*, Blackwell 1984.

30. See futher MacNutt, op. cit., ch. 8.

31. See John Wimber, *Power Healing*, Hodder and Stoughton 1986, ch. 8.

32. Rex Gardner, *Healing Miracles*, Darton, Longman and Todd 1986, ch. 9. The chapter is entitled 'God's Strange Work'.

33. Thus the famous evangelist David Watson died from his cancer but firmly believed that he had received inner healing. See David Watson, *Fear No Evil*, Hodder and Stoughton 1984.

34. See, e.g., Watson, op. cit.; Frances Parsons, *Pools of Living Water*, Triangle 1987.

35. See further, e.g., Jerome D. Frank, *Persuasion and Healing*, New York: Shocken 1974.

36. Wright records of one charismatic healer, 'He does not appear to face honest failure. The accounts of his spectacular cures leave one slightly anxious as to the fate of those who have been to him, and whilst they have may have experienced temporary help or relief, have not been physically cured. He is strangely silent about such people.' (Frank Wright, *The Pastoral Nature of Healing*, SCM Press 1985.) It is usual for any healing system to have mechanisms for coping with failure in such a way that particular episodes of disappointment do not undermine faith in the whole system. Compare, for example, the witchdoctors of the Azande tribe in Africa. People are sceptical of the individual competence of witchdoctors and can accept their failures even as they continue to believe in the potency of the witchdoctor's art in general. See further E. E. Evans Pritchard, *Witchcraft, Oracles and Magic among the Azande*, Oxford University Press 1976.

37. See further, e.g. Norman Cohn, *The Pursuit of the Millenium*, Granada 1970; Ronald A. Knox, *Enthusiasm*, Oxford University Press 1950, Collins 1987.

38. Kelsey, op. cit.

39. See further, e.g. Wesley Carr, *Brief Encounters*, SPCK 1985, chs 3 and 4; John Habgood, *Church and Nation in a Secular Age*, Darton, Longman and Todd 1983, especially chs 5 and 6; Michael Hill, *A Sociology of Religion*, Heinemann 1973, chs 3 and 4; Betty Scharf, *The Sociological Study of Religion*, Hutchinson 1970, ch. 5.

40. See further, e.g., Craig Dykstra, *Vision and Character*, New York: Paulist Press 1981; Habgood, op. cit.; Stanley Hauerwas, *A Community of Character*, University of Notre Dame Press 1981; George Stroup, *The Promise of Narrative Theology*, SCM Press 1984.

41. See Alan D. Gilbert, *The Making of Post-Christian Britain*, Longman 1980; Habgood, op. cit., ch. 1; Bryan Wilson, *Religion in a Secular Society*, Penguin 1969.

42. See further Anthony Russell, *The Clerical Profession*, SPCK 1980.

43. See further Peter L. Berger, *The Heretical Imperative*, Collins 1980.

44. Jesus sent his disciples out to preach, teach and heal. This threefold ministry remains essential, especially in evangelical and charismatic churches where the occurrence of healing is seen as verification of the teaching and preaching.

45. See further Russell, op. cit.

46. I owe this insight to a conversation with Dr Bryan Wilson of All Souls' College, Oxford.

47. Harrell, op. cit., makes very clear the prominence of the financial and show business aspects of healing ministries in the USA where healing is a profitable industry.

48. See Jeremy Rifkin, *The Emerging Order*, New York: Ballantine 1979, p. 148.

49. See, e.g., John Wimber, op. cit., *Power Evangelism*, Hodder and Stoughton 1985.

50. Dorothee Sölle writes: 'We Protestants reduced our symbols and confined them to ourselves, to our personalities. We used religious concepts and images for one purpose only: they had to serve the supreme value of middle class culture – individualism. . . . Religion becomes a tool of the ruling classes, and only continues to function in order to comfort the sad, enrich personal life, and give the individual the feeling of significance. Sin then becomes personal transgressions. . . . The cross then becomes my unique suffering and the resurrection my individual immortality.' (Dorothee Sölle, *Choosing Life*, SCM Press 1981, p. 82.)

51. See further, e.g., Steven Lukes, *Individualism*, Blackwell 1973; Stephen Pattison, *A Critique of Pastoral Care*, SCM Press 1988, ch. 5; Howard B. Waitzkin and Barbara Waterman, *The Exploitation of Illness in Capitalist Society*, Indianapolis: Bobbs-Merrill 1974. Paul Halmos, *The Personal and the Political*, Hutchinson 1978, demonstrates how all helping and therapeutic activities in our society also work mainly within the individualist paradigm.

52. See Rifkin, op. cit., also Hollenweger, op. cit., ch. 31, Douglas Davies, 'The Charismatic Ethic and the Spirit of Post-Industrialism' in David Martin and Peter Mullen (eds), *Strange Gifts?*, Blackwell 1984.

53. For more on the disenchantment of the universe see, e.g., Peter L. Berger, *A Rumour of Angels*, Penguin 1971; *The Social Reality of Religion*, Penguin 1973; Peter L. Berger, Brigitte Berger and Hans Kellner, *The Homeless Mind*, Penguin 1974.

54. Hollenweger, *The Pentecostals*, p. 467.

55. See Terence Ranger, 'Introduction' in W. J. Sheils (ed.) *The Church and Healing*, Blackwell 1982.

56. Smith, op. cit., p. 416.

57. See, e.g., Wilson, *Health is for People*.

58. De-contextualization may, in fact, be a very important factor in some kinds of effective healing. Following Turner and Turner, op. cit, Easthope, op. cit. suggests that leaving familiar surroundings and entering into a liminal

state where new forces are encountered and new identities can be assumed may be very necessary.

59. See Easthope, op. cit.

60. See futher, e.g., David Tuckett, 'Doctors and Patients' in David Tuckett (ed.), *An Introduction to Medical Sociology*, Tavistock 1976. While Christianity adheres to asymmetric power relationships in healing there is little scope for healers to learn anything from ill people or for the latter to contribute anything to their own healing. This lack of mutuality is a deeply worrying aspect of the religious healing movement, as well as of secular healing relationships.

61. But see works cited above by Lambourne, Maddocks and Wilson.

62. See futher, e.g., Brown, op. cit.; Gardner, op. cit.; Kelsey, op. cit. More references to works on miracles can be found in ch. 1, n. 4.

63. The characterization of modern theology advanced here is based to quite a large extent on Alfredo Fierro, *The Militant Gospel*, SCM Press 1977, ch. 1.

64. This is particularly true of the liberation and political theologies. See, e.g., Gustavo Gutiérrez, *A Theology of Liberation*, SCM Press 1974; Alastair Kee (ed.), *A Reader in Political Theology*, SCM Press 1974; *The Scope of Political Theology*, SCM Press 1978.

65. See further, e.g., Grace M. Jantzen, *God's World, God's Body*, Darton, Longman and Todd 1984; McFague, op. cit.

66. For more on practical theology see, e.g., Paul H. Ballard (ed.), *The Foundations of Pastoral Studies and Practical Theology*, Faculty of Theology, University College, Cardiff 1986, Don S. Browning (ed.), *Practical Theology*, San Francisco: Harper and Row 1983.

67. Some of these questions are addressed in Wilson, *The Church is Healing*.

68. See MacNutt, op. cit., chs 2 and 3.

69. See futher Gordon D. Kaufman, *God the Problem*, Harvard University Press 1972, especially ch. 6; *Theology for a Nuclear Age*, Manchester University Press 1985; Maurice Wiles, *God's Action in the World*, SCM Press 1986. For Similar views to those of Wiles and Kaufman see McFague, op. cit. For a considered but more interventionist view of the deity see Michael Langford, *Providence*, SCM Press 1981. For a thoroughgoing defence of direct divine action see Vernon White, *The Fall of a Sparrow*, Paternoster 1985.

70. See further Jürgen Moltmann, *The Crucified God*, SCM Press 1974.

71. This kind of argument is advanced in, e.g., Richard Harries, *Christianity and War in a Nuclear Age*, Mowbray 1986.

72. See Kaufman, *Theology for a Nuclear Age*; McFague, op. cit.

73. See further A. L. Cochrane, *Effectiveness and Efficiency*, Nuffield Provincial Hospitals Trust 1971.

74. I discuss harming in care in Pattison, op. cit., ch. 7. See also Bill Jordan, *Helping in Social Work*, Routledge and Kegan Paul 1979.

75. See Leslie Houlden, *Connections*, SCM Press 1986.

76. See Peter Townsend and Nick Davidson (eds), *Inequalities in Health*, Penguin 1988.

77. See works cited above by Lambourne and Wilson.

4. *Politics, Conflict, Healing and Illness*

1. See, e.g., James C. McGilvray, *The Quest for Health and Wholeness*, Tübingen: German Institute for Medical Mission 1981; Morris Maddocks, *The Christian Healing Ministry*, SPCK 1981; John A Sanford, *Healing and Wholeness*, New York: Paulist Press 1977.

2. William H. McNeill, *Plagues and Peoples*, Penguin 1979, p. 13.

3. See, e.g., E. P. Sanders, *Jesus and Judaism*, SCM Press 1985; Gerd Theissen, *Sociology of Early Palestinian Christianity*, Philadelphia: Fortress Press 1978; *The Shadow of the Galilean*, SCM Press 1987. Compare also Albert Nolan, *Jesus Before Christianity*, Darton, Longman and Todd 1977; Morton Smith, *Jesus the Magician*, Aquarian 1985; Geza Vermes, *Jesus the Jew*, Collins 1976, rev. ed. SCM Press 1983.

4. Theissen, *Sociology of Early Palestinian Christianity*, p. 36.

5. Compare Norman Cohn, *The Pursuit of the Millenium*, Granada 1970. Introduction.

6. See further works cited above by Sanders and Theissen. Smith, op. cit., suggests that Jesus used his healing in much the same way as North American evangelists in our own day do, i.e. to attract attention for his message. This interpretation is congruent with Jesus being seen by his own contemporaries within the general role of eschatological prophet. For a resume of this kind of thinking see, e.g., Sanders, op. cit., p. 173.

7. See further I. M. Lewis, *Ecstatic Religion*, Penguin 1971; David Martin, 'The Political Oeconomy of the Holy Spirit' in David Martin and Peter Mullen (eds), *Strange Gifts?*, Blackwell 1984. I shall develop this point further below. See also ch. 3 n. 27.

8. See further Sanders, especially p. 173.

9. See especially R. A. Lambourne, *Community, Church and Healing*, Darton, Longman and Todd 1963.

10. For more on the idea that Jesus was possessed by a spirit like a shaman see Smith, op. cit. Smith suggests that Paul, too, can be perceived as being possessed by a spirit, in his case the spirit of Jesus, hence his references to living in Christ and having Christ within him.

11. See further Mary Douglas, *Purity and Danger*, Routledge and Kegan Paul 1970.

12. For more on the charismatic authority of doctors see M. W. Susser and W. Watson, *Sociology in Medicine*, Oxford University Press 1971, ch. 7; Eliot Freidson, *Profession of Medicine*, New York: Dodds Mead 1975.

13. See Lewis, op. cit., *Religion in Context*, Cambridge University Press 1986.

14. For more on this interpretation see Smith, op. cit. The ambivalence of possessing spirits is explored in M. A. Screech, 'Good Madness in

Christendom' in W. F. Bynum, Roy Porter and Michael Shepherd (eds), *The Anatomy of Madness*, Tavistock 1985.

15. See further Eamon Duffy, 'Valentine Greatrakes, The Irish Stroker: Miracle, Science and Orthodoxy in Restoration England' in K. Robbins (ed.), *Religion and Humanism*, Blackwell 1981; Keith Thomas, *Religion and the Decline of Magic*, Penguin 1973, ch. 7. Thomas, op. cit., gives background to the link between magic, miraculous healing and social unrest in the sixteenth and seventeenth centuries. See especially ch. 3.

16. See Thomas, op. cit., ch. 3. Ronald A. Knox, *Enthusiasm*, Collins 1987, provides some background for Quakerism and the Wesleyan movement.

17. See further David E. Harrell, *All Things are Possible*, University of Indiana Press 1975.

18. See pp. 28ff. above.

19. Lewis, *Ecstatic Religion*, ch. 1. Lewis also ascribes this form of protest to people of both sexes in the lowest classes of traditional societies.

20. Lewis, op. cit., p. 32.

21. Rudolph M. Bell, *Holy Anorexia*, University of Chicago Press 1985.

22. Roy Porter, *A Social History of Insanity*, Weidenfield and Nicolson 1987.

23. See, e.g., Dorothy Rowe, *Depression*, Routledge and Kegan Paul 1983.

24. See 'The Sacred Disease' in G. E. R. Lloyd (ed.), *Hippocratic Writings*, Penguin 1979. These paragraphs owe much to Darrel W. Amundsen and Gary B. Ferngren, 'Medicine and Religion: Early Christianity Through the Middle Ages' in Martin E. Marty and Kenneth L. Vaux, *Health/Medicine and the Faith Traditions*, Philadelphia: Fortress Press 1982.

25. Henry Sigerist, quoted in Amundsen and Ferngren, op. cit.

26. See further Morton H. Kelsey, *Healing and Christianity*, SCM Press 1973, chs 8 and 9.

27. See further Amundsen and Ferngren, op. cit.

28. Lucinda McCray Beier, *Sufferers and Healers*, Routledge and Kegan Paul 1987, points out that most people as recently as the seventeenth century were probably aware of discomfort and the symptoms of illness most of the time.

29. See further, e.g., Margaret Pelling and Charles Webster, 'Medical Practitioners' in Charles Webster (ed.), *Health, Medicine and Mortality in the Sixteenth Century*, Cambridge University Press 1979.

30. See Pelling and Webster, op. cit., Michael Macdonald *Mystical Bedlam*, Cambridge University Press 1981. The latter work explores the work of one particular cleric/physician/astrologer/healer.

31. See Anthony Russell, *The Clerical Profession*, SPCK 1980. Sydney Smith and Parson Woodforde, for example, both had some medical training.

32. See further, e.g., Frank Mort, *Dangerous Sexualities*, Routledge and Kegan Paul 1987, ch. 1. Compare Carlo Cipolla, *Faith, Reason and the Plague*, Harvester Press 1979, which explores the way in which church and state ended up working against each other in seventeenth-century Italy. Civic

authorities tried to enforce quarantine regulations while the church called the faithful to break them in order to gather together for prayer,.

33. See Allan Brandt, *No Magic Bullet*, Oxford University Press 1987.

34. See Appendix B below for more on the contemporary state of the relationship between religion and medicine.

35. See further, e.g., Michael Wilson, *Health is for People*, Darton, Longman and Todd 1975.

36. See further Appendix B below.

37. Herbert Hensley Henson, *Notes on Spiritual Healing*, Williams and Norgate 1925.

38. See further Stuart Mews, 'The Revival of Spiritual Healing in the Church of England' in W. J. Sheils (ed.), *The Church and Healing*, Blackwell 1982.

39. Peter Townsend and Nick Davidson, *Inequalities in Health*, Penguin 1988.

40. See below pp. 123ff. for more on this and the evidence upon which my assertions are based.

41. See further Derek Fraser, *The Evolution of the British Welfare State*, Macmillan 1973, p. 218; Frank Honigsbaum, *The Division in British Medicine*, Kogan Page 1979; Vicente Navarro, *Class Struggle, the State and Medicine*, Martin Robertson 1978.

42. See further, e.g., Rudolf Klein, *The Politics of the National Health Service*, Longman 1973; Vivienne Walters, *Class Inequalities and Health Care*, Croom Helm 1980; Ivan Illich, *Limits to Medicine*, Marion Boyars 1976.

43. See further, e.g., Rudolf Klein, op. cit. There are many accessible and interesting books on the present conflicts in the Health Service and their practical effects. See, e.g., Nick Davidson, *A Question of Care*, Michael Joseph 1987.

44. See further, e.g., Susser and Watson, op. cit., ch. 7. For more on conflicts of goals in practice in psychiatric hospitals see, e.g., Erving Goffman, *Asylums;* Kathleen Jones and Roy Sidebotham, *Mental Hospitals at Work*, Routledge and Kegan Paul 1962.

45. See Susser and Watson, op. cit., ch. 7.

46. For a comprehensive and incisive analysis of the workforce in the NHS and the power relations engendered within it see Margaret Stacey, *The Sociology of Health and Healing*, Unwin Hyman 1988, chs 13, 14 and 15.

47. A summary of the reports of commissions of enquiry set up to investigate scandalous conditions in psychiatric hospitals during the 1970s can be found in Virginia Beardshaw, *Conscientious Objectors at Work*, Social Audit 1981. See also J. P. Martin, *Hospitals in Trouble*, Blackwell 1984; Stephen Pattison, 'Pastoral care in psychiatric hospitals: An approach based on some of the insights and methods of liberation theology', unpublished PhD diss., University of Edinburgh 1982.

48. Freidson, op. cit., p. 94.

49. For more on the conflictual/negotiative relationship between patients

and doctors see Freidson, op. cit.; G. Stimpson and B. Webb, *Going to see the Doctor*, Routledge and Kegan Paul 1978.

50. See further Gary Easthorpe, *Healers and Alternative Medicine*, Gower 1986.

51. See George W. Brown and Tirril Harris, *Social Origins of Depression*, Tavistock 1978.

52. In August B. Hollingshead and Fredrick C. Redlich, *Social Class and Mental Illness*, New York: John Wiley 1958, it is asserted that 'Class IV and V family members regard mental illnesses as somatic diseases' (op. cit., p. 341). See also Robert A. Moore, Elissa P. Benedek, and John G. Wallace, 'Social class, schizophrenia and the psychiatrist', *American Journal of Psychiatry 120*, 1963–4, pp. 149–54, which shows that lower class women see mental disorder in physical terms unlike upper class women and their doctors who see mental disorder more in psychological terms. This is amplified in Dewitt L. Crandell and Bruce P. Dohrenwend, 'Some relations among psychiatric symptoms, organic illness and social class', *American Journal of Psychiatry 123*, 1967, pp. 1527–38. Crandell and Dohrenwend write, 'There is a distinct tendency on the part of lower-class groups to express psychological distress in physiological terms' (op. cit., p. 1536). All these findings, though North American in origin, are consistent with lower class women's views of illness found in this country. See further, e.g., Jocelyn Cornwell, *Hard-earned Lives*, Tavistock 1984. In that study, Cornwell found that women saw illness as coming from outside themselves and so felt they could do nothing to prevent or cure it by their own actions or habits.

53. See Brown and Harris, op. cit., ch. 16.

54. See Rowe, op. cit.

55. I owe this insight to the Rev. John Hodgkinson, formerly a student at Edinburgh Theological College.

56. See, e.g., Francis MacNutt, *Healing*, Notre Dame: Ave Maria Press 1974.

57. Nolan, op. cit., p. 32.

58. Faith as concrete human action for change is a main theme of contemporary political theologies. See. e.g., Dorothee Sölle, *Choosing Life*, SCM Press 1981.

5. *Responding to Mental Illness*

1. George Rosen, *Madness in Society*, University of Chicago Press 1980, p. 101. For examples of the different manifestations of mental disorder in different cultures see, e.g., Ari Kiev, *Transcultural Psychiatry*, Penguin 1972.

2. See further David Cohen, *Forgotten Millions*, Paladin 1988, ch. 1, Richmond Fellowship, *Mental Health and the Community*, Richmond Fellowship Press 1983, p. vii.

3. I discuss the practical and theoretical challenge of mentally ill people to the churches somewhat differently and more thoroughly in Stephen Pattison,

'Mentally ill people: a challenge to the churches', *Modern Churchman* 29, 1986, pp. 28–38.

4. For the meanings of these terms see, e.g., Richard B. Fisher, *A Dictionary of Mental Health*, Granada 1980.

5. The account here is largely based on Rosen, op. cit., chs 2 and 3. See also Roy Porter, *A Social History of Insanity*, Weidenfeld and Nicolson 1987, ch. 2.

6. Arguably, R. D. Laing's view of mental disorder as privileged, meaningful but indirect and ambivalent communication is a continuation of the idea of good or mystical madness. See, e.g., R. D. Laing, *The Divided Self*, Tavistock 1960; *Sanity, Madness and the Family*, Tavistock 1964.

7. M. A. Screech, 'Good Madness in Christendom, in W. F. Bynum, Roy Porter and Michael Shepherd (eds), *The Anatomy of Madness*, Tavistock 1985, p. 25.

8. See I Corinthians 1.

9. See Erasmus, *The Praise of Folly*, Penguin 1971.

10. See further, e.g., Peter Brown, 'Sorcery, Demons and the Rise of Christianity: From Late Antiquity into the Middle Ages' in Peter Brown, *Religion and Society in the Age of Saint Augustine*, Faber 1972; Michael Dols, 'Insanity in Byzantine and Islamic Medicine', *Dumbarton Oaks Papers 38*, 1984, pp. 135–48.

11. See Basil Clarke, *Mental Disorder in Earlier Britain*, University of Wales Press 1975. See John Saward, *Perfect Fools*, Oxford University Press 1980, for an account of holy folly down the ages.

12. Screech, op. cit., p. 37.

13. See further, e.g., Patricia Allderidge, 'Management and mismanagement at Bedlam, 1547–1633' in Charles Webster (ed.), *Health, Medicine and Mortality in the Sixteenth Century*, Cambridge University Press 1979; Clarke, op. cit., ch. 5; Kathleen Jones, *A History of the Mental Health Services*, Routledge and Kegan Paul 1972.

14. Cf. Rosen, op. cit., p. 88.

15. Michael MacDonald, *Mystical Bedlam*, Cambridge University Press 1981.

16. Ibid., chs 4 and 5.

17. Roy Porter, *Mind Forg'd Manacles*, Athlone Press 1987, p. x.

18. Ibid., p. 54.

19. Ibid., p. 227.

20. For more on eighteenth- and nineteenth-century treatments of the insane and their underlying ideologies see, e.g., Porter, *Mind Forg'd Manacles*, chs 3 and 4; Joan Busfield, *Managing Madness*, Hutchinson 1986, chs 6 and 7; Vieda Skultans, *English Madness*, Routledge and Kegan Paul 1979.

21. See Busfield, op. cit., ch. 5.

22. See further Anne Digby, *Madness, Morality and Medicine*, Cambridge University Press 1985. This provides a history of The Retreat. Fiona Godlee, 'Aspects of nonconformity: Quakers and the lunatic fringe; in W. F. Bynum,

Roy Porter and Michael Shepherd (eds.), *The Anatomy of Madness*, Tavistock 1985, points out the irony that Quakers should end up controlling lunacy when early members of their own movement were perceived as social and religious non-conformists and therefore persecuted and disqualified as madmen.

23. For the development of the asylum in the nineteenth century see Busfield, op. cit.; Jones, op. cit.; Andrew T. Scull, *Museums of Madness*, Allen Lane 1979.

24. See Scull, op. cit., chs 4 and 5.

25. See further, e.g., DHSS, *Better Services for the Mentally Ill*, HMSO, Cmnd 6233, 1975; Andrew T. Scull, *Decarceration*, Englewood Cliffs: Prentice Hall 1977.

26. For this historical interpretation see Scull, *Museums of Madness*.

27. See ibid., chs 4 and 5 for this interpretation. Doctors had no especially effective remedies for mental disorder in the nineteenth century but ended up establishing their dominance on the basis or moral therapy, a system perfected by laymen.

28. Some of the comments made on psychiatric hospitals in recent years are apposite here. Belknap writes, 'Against continual deficits of staff and materiel (sic), and against occasional instances of indifference and neglect, or outright abuse, progress had been made from time to time; but the uneasy feeling exists that reform and regression in mental hospital affairs are inseparable processes. The cycle has repeated itself too often to be fortuitous. The sequence of expose, reform, progress, indifference, apathy and decline has been repeated with variations in a dozen states of the Union in the past twenty years.' (Ivan Belknap, *Human Problems of a State Mental Hospital*, New York: McGraw Hill 1956, pp. vii-viii.) Talbott writes, 'It should be obvious by now that state hospitals, as they are currently constituted, do not work, seem designed not to work, and have never worked . . . Critics . . . continue to point out the problems, decade after decade, without any perceivable effect.' (John A. Talbott, *The Death of the Asylum*, New York: Grune and Stratton 1978, p. 125.) It should, however, be noted that whatever the scientific and intellectual validity of various treatment systems, the most bizarre methods do appear to have had some beneficial effect. See further MacDonald, op. cit., for curious treatments which do actually seem to have made some patients well.

29. There are several good books which describe and assess the various models of mental disorder outlined below. See, e.g., Peter Hill, Robin Murray and Anthony Thorley (eds), *Essentials of Postgraduate Psychiatry*, Academic Press 1979; Miriam Siegler and Humphrey Osmond, *Models of Madness, Models of Medicine*, New York: Macmillan 1974; Stuart Sutherland, *Breakdown*, Granada 1977; Peter Tyrer and Derek Steinberg, *Models of Mental Disorder*, John Wiley 1987.

30. Tyrer and Steinberg, op. cit., p. 9.

31. Syphilitic paralysis and senile dementia (Alzheimer's Disease) seem,

prima facie, to have a clear organic basis, even if other factors also bear on their incidence and cure. See further, e.g., Barry Reisberg, *A Guide to Alzheimer's Disease*, New York: Free Press 1981.

32. Anthony Clare, *Psychiatry in Dissent*, Tavistock 1976, p. 44. For further discussion of the disease model of mental disorder see, e.g., Anthony Clare, 'The Disease Model in Psychiatry' in Hill, Murray and Thorley (eds), op. cit.; R. E. Kendell, *The Role of Diagnosis in Psychiatry*, Blackwell 1975; and especially, J. K. Wing, *Reasoning About Madness*, Oxford University Press 1978.

33. See further, e.g., Nigel Goldie, 'Psychiatry and the Medical Mandate' in Michael Wadsworth and David Robinson (eds), *Studies in Everyday Medical Life*, Martin Robertson 1976.

34. For a critique of this see Geoff Baruch and Andrew Treacher, *Psychiatry Observed*, Routledge and Kegan Paul 1978.

35. See pp. 30ff. above, also, e.g., Peter Conrad and Joseph W. Schneider, *Deviance and Medicalization*, St Louis: Mosby 1980.

36. See further, e.g., Paul Halmos, *The Personal and the Political*, Hutchinson 1978.

37. See further Sutherland, op. cit., ch. 18; Paul Bebbington, 'Behaviour Therapy' in Hill, Murray and Thorley (eds), op. cit.

38. See further David H. Clark, *Administrative Therapy*, Tavistock 1964; *Social Therapy in Psychiatry*, Penguin 1981; R. D. Hinshelwood and Nick Manning (eds), *Therapeutic Communities*, Routledge and Kegan Paul 1979.

39. Clark, *Administrative Therapy*, p. 68.

40. Sutherland, op. cit., p. 177. This comment brings to mind Stanton and Schwartz's assertion that, 'a mental hospital is a place where ordinary civil liberties are called privileges'. (A. G. Stanton and M. S. Schwartz, *The Mental Hospital*, New York: Basic Books 1954, p. 244.)

41. Compare, e.g., Gerard Egan, *The Skilled Helper*, Monterey, California: Brooks Cole 1982. This book is behaviourally oriented and is a standard work for organizations like the English Marriage Guidance Council (now called RELATE).

42. Cf. Anthony Storr, *The Art of Psychotherapy*, Secker and Warburg and Heinemann 1979. See also Warren Kinston and Rachel Rosser, 'Individual Psychotherapy' in Hill, Murray and Thorley (eds), op. cit.; Dennis Brown and Jonathan Pedder, *Introduction to Psychotherapy*, Tavistock 1979; Tyrer and Steinberg, op. cit., ch. 3.

43. See. e.g., John Cobb, 'Group Interaction' in Hill, Murray and Thorley (eds), op. cit.

44. For the perceived and actual superiority of the therapist see, e.g., Paul Halmos, *The Faith of the Counsellors*, Constable 1965.

45. Malcolm Jeeves, 'Christian belief, experience and practice in the light of expanding psychological knowledge' in Malcolm Jeeves (ed.), *The Behavioural Sciences: A Christian Perspective*, Inter Varsity Press 1984, points up the lack of evidence for the effectiveness of psychotherapy and psycho-

analysis. He also puzzles as to why Christians have become so fascinated with this very particular and very ambiguous type of psychology.

46. Doris C. Gilbert and Daniel J. Levinson, ' "Custodialism" and "Humanism" in Mental Hospital Structure and in Staff Ideology' in Milton Greenblatt, Daniel J. Levinson and Richard H. Williams (eds), *The Patient and the Mental Hospital*, Glencoe: Free Press 1957, p. 22.

47. See further, e.g., Russell Barton, *Institutional Neuroses*, Wright 1977; Erving Goffman, *Asylums*, Penguin 1968; J. K. Wing and G. W. Brown, *Institutionalism and Schizophrenia*, Cambridge University Press 1970.

48. See further, e.g., Martin, op. cit.

49. See further, e.g., DHSS, op. cit.

50. David Mechanic, *Mental Health and Social Policy*, Englewood Cliffs: Prentice Hall 1980, p. 20. See also Cohen, op. cit., ch. 4.

51. See further Scull, *Decarceration*, p. 153; J. K. Wing and Rolf Olsen (eds), *Community Care for the Mentally Disabled*, Oxford University Press 1979.

52. For critiques of the policy of community care and the values it embodies see, e.g., Stephen Pattison and Paul Armitage, 'An ethical analysis of the policies of British community and hospital care for mentally ill people', *Journal of Medical Ethics* 12, 1986, pp. 136–42; Alan Walker (ed.), *Community Care*, Blackwell and Robertson 1982.

53. Kathleen Jones, John Brown and Jonathan Bradshaw, *Issues in Social Policy*, Routledge and Kegan Paul 1978, p. 114.

54. Thomas J. Scheff, *Being Mentally Ill*, Chicago: Aldine 1966, ch. 2.

55. These assertions are based on Scheff, op. cit.

56. For more on stigma and stigmatization see, e.g., Erving Goffman, *Stigma*, Penguin 1968. On a practical note, one of the most useful things that contemporary Christians could do to equip themselves for caring work in the world is to come to understand this notion of stigma and the rejection which it implies. If we understand why we shy away from people who are mentally ill, have AIDS, are a different colour from ourselves, or have different values, we start to be in a position where we might be able to help them – and ourselves. The single most useful education programme that any church congregation or seminary could run would be one on stigma. Of course, the idea of stigma is richly suggestive theologically. Could it be that the whole of theological education, as well as pastoral education, might be centred round a multi-disciplinary, practical, theoretical, experiential and theological exploration of stigma?

57. See Conrad and Schneider, op. cit., ch. 2.

58. See Paul Rock, *Deviant Behaviour*, Hutchinson 1973, pp. 47ff.; Agnes Miles, *The Mentally Ill in Contemporary Society*, Martin Robertson 1981, pp. 188ff.

59. See Conrad and Schneider, op. cit., p. 6; Thomas Szasz, *Law, Liberty and Psychiatry*, Routledge and Kegan Paul 1974, pp. 46ff.

60. David L. Rosenham, 'On Being Sane in Insane Places' in Alfred Dean,

Alan M. Kraft and Bert Pepper (eds), *The Social Setting of Mental Health*, New York: Basic Books 1976.

61. The merits of an eclectic approach from the psychiatrist's point of view are considered in Clare, *Psychiatry in Dissent*, ch. 2.

62. I discuss this further in my *A Critique of Pastoral Care*, SCM Press 1988, ch. 4. See also, e.g., Irving K. Zola, 'Medicine as an Institution of Social Control' in John Ehrenreich (ed.), *The Cultural Crisis of Modern Medicine*, New York: Monthly Review Press 1978.

63. For introductory material on liberation theologies see, e.g., Rosino Gibellini (ed.), *Frontiers of Theology in Latin America*, SCM Press 1980; Gustavo Gutiérrez, *A Theology of Liberation*, SCM Press 1974; Alastair Kee (ed.), *A Reader in Political Theology*, SCM Press 1974; *The Scope of Political Theology*, SCM Press 1978.

64. See further George W. Brown and Tirril Harris, *The Social Origins of Depression*, Tavistock 1978; Melvin L. Kohn, 'Social Class and Schizophrenia – A Critical Review and Reformulation' in P. M. Roman and H. R. Trice, *Explorations in Social Psychiatry*, Philadelphia: F. A. Davies 1974; Richard Warner, *Recovery from Schizophrenia*, Routledge and Kegan Paul 1985.

65. See Miles, op. cit., ch. 7.

66. See further, e.g., Elaine Showalter, *The Female Malady*, Virago 1987; Elizabeth Howell and Marjorie Bayes (eds), *Women and Mental Health*, New York: Basic Books 1981.

67. See Brown and Harris, op. cit., ch. 15.

68. Cohen, op. cit., p. 211. See also R. Littlewood and M. Lipsedge, *Aliens and Alienists*, Penguin 1982.

69. See Harvey M. Brenner, *Mental Illness and the Economy*, Harvard University Press 1973; Richard Smith, *Unemployment and Health*, Oxford University Press 1987, chs 5, 6, and 7.

70. Cohen, op. cit., p. 212.

71. Anthony Clare, *Psychiatry in Dissent*, second ed., Tavistock 1980, p. 396.

72. Robert Holman, *Poverty*, Martin Robertson 1978, p. 28.

73. Cohen comments, 'In Britain when you enter a prison you are read a list of your duties and rights. Enter a mental hospital in most parts of the world and nothing similar happens.' (Cohen, op. cit., p. 30.)

74. John A. Talbott, *The Death of the Asylum*, New York: Grune and Stratton 1978, p. 68. My emphasis.

75. Clare, *Psychiatry in Dissent*, second ed., p. 400. This is a dated statistic but the point it is cited to support is still valid.

76. See further Beardshaw, op. cit.; Martin, op. cit.

77. See South East Thames Regional Health Authority, *Report of a Committee of Enquiry, St Augustine's Hospital, Chartham, Canterbury*, SE Thames Regional Health Authority 1976.

78. See further Brian Abel-Smith, *National Health Service – The First Thirty Years*, HMSO 1978; Peter Ryan, 'Residential Care for the Mentally

Disabled' in Wing and Olsen (eds), op. cit. The short-fall in resources for community care of the mentally ill is frequently highlighted by public bodies concerned about mental health welfare. In their report, *Mental Health in the Community*, the Richmond Fellowship concluded that, 'Insofar as shelter, asylum, security, basic security and care are still required on a long-term basis . . . it is now difficult to find appropriate places. The wide range of substitute provisions – hostels, group homes, subsidised housing, domiciliary supervision, day centres, rehabilitation and sheltered workshops – has not been established on an adequate scale and the current climate, both financial and vocational is not favourable. Social Service departments are competing for scarce funds and have to allocate their slender resources according to their own priorities, among which the mentally ill have a lowly place. The voluntary organisations do their utmost to meet the need, but their resources, too, are severely limited. Where services are inadequate, *the relatives and the afflicted have to cope as best they can.*' (Richmond Fellowship, op. cit., p. 6. My emphasis.)

79. Cohen, op. cit., p. 220.

80. It looks as if in the community, where they will be more widely dispersed, mentally ill people will be even more invisible and politically insignificant than they were in the old hospitals.

81. For more on the importance and practicalities of developing a practical 'bias to the poor' see, e.g., my *A Critique of Pastoral Care*, ch. 5; Laurie Green, *Power to the Powerless*, Marshall Pickering 1987; Dieter T. Hessell, *Social Ministry*, Philadelphia: Westminster Press 1982; David Shepherd, *Bias to the Poor*, Hodder and Stoughton 1983.

6. The Judgment of AIDS

1. This chapter is substantially the same title which first appeared in *Contact* 94, 1987, pp. 26–32. I have added some paragraphs and notes. It is reproduced here by kind permission of the editor of *Contact*.

2. Allan Brandt, *No Magic Bullet*, Oxford University Press 1987, p. 191. This is an excellent and fascinating history of attitudes to venereal diseases in the USA in the present century.

3. Peter Slack, *The Impact of Plague in Tudor and Stuart England*, Routledge and Kegan Paul 1985, p. 4.

4. By the end of April 1988, 1,417 people had developed AIDS in its full-blown form, 839 people had died with the syndrome and 8,443 people had been found to be HIV positive. DHSS, *AIDS Briefing*, AIDS Unit, DHSS, May 1988.

5. At the time of writing (summer 1988), a majority of deaths from AIDS in the West Midlands came from the haemophiliac population.

6. This chapter is parochial insofar as it only deals with the judgment of AIDS in the UK. AIDS is already a massive scourge, for example, in Africa.

7. The unfortunate tendency of some Christians to use horrific epidemics for their own moral purposes is well shown historically in R. J. Morris, *Cholera*

1832, Croom Helm 1976. Morris writes, 'such terrible afflictions as cholera could only be seen as a form of punishment . . . for sin against the wishes of an all-powerful God. Thus pain and death became explicable, legitimate and more bearable.' (Op. cit., p. 132).

8. See above pp. 41ff.

9. See above pp.40f., 65ff.

10. See futher, e.g., Alastair V. Campbell, *The Gospel of Anger*, SPCK 1986; Jim Garrison, *The Darkness of God*, SCM Press 1982.

11. Just because Jesus is portrayed as having particular attitudes or doing particular acts does not mean that we have to imitate his example exactly. The pictures of Jesus provided by the gospel writers, must, however, serve as a question mark to our present attitudes and practices.

12. For this point see any introductory book on ethics, e.g., Peter Baelz, *Ethics and Belief*, Sheldon 1977.

13. In E. P. Sanders, *Jesus and Judaism*, SCM Press 1985; Gerd Theissen, *The Shadow of the Galilean*, SCM Press 1987, it is suggested that the reason Jesus infuriated the religious establishment is because he actually did not require sinners to repent in order to partake in the Kingdom of God. All they had to do was to believe his message.

14. Behavioural psychologists have long recognized that reward is a much better way of engendering and maintaining desired behaviour than punishment. See further, e.g., Leonard Kristal, *Understanding Psychology*, Harper and Row 1979, ch. 3.

15. Philip Siegler, *The Black Death*, Penguin 1970. There are many good and interesting works on historical responses to plague. See, e.g., op. cit.; Anne Carmichael, *Plague and the Poor in Renaissance Florence*, Cambridge University Press 1986; Carlo M. Cipolla, *Faith, Reason and the Plague*, Harvester Press 1979; William H. MacNeill, *Plagues and Peoples*, Penguin 1979; Open University, *Medical Knowledge: Doubt and Certainty*, Open University Press 1985, chs 5 and 6. All of these, together with René Dubos, *The White Plague*, Rutgers University Press 1987, (a work on tuberculosis), emphasizes the fact that human and social responses to diseases crucially affect their course and spread. A contemporary history of AIDS in the USA can be found in Randy Shilts, *And The Band Played On*, Penguin 1987.

16. The selfishness and moral indifference of influential social groups in times of epidemic is well described in relation to the nineteenth-century cholera epidemics in Morris, op. cit..

17. See above pp. 35ff.

18. One of the very positive bi-products of the advent of AIDS has been the growth of an excellent literature of sexuality, disease, values and metaphors. See, e.g., Peter Aggleton and Hilary Homans (eds), *Social Aspects of AIDS*, Falmer 1988; Dennis Altman, *AIDS and the New Puritanism*, Pluto Press 1986; Jack Babuscio, *We Speak for Ourselves*, SPCK 1988; Brandt, op. cit.; Sandy L. Gilman, *Disease and Representation*, Cornell University Press 1988; Frank Mort, *Dangerous Sexualities*, Routledge and Kegan Paul 1987;

Jeffrey Weeks, *Sexuality and its Discontents*, Routledge and Kegan Paul 1985; *Sexuality*, Tavistock 1986; Simon Watney, *Policing Desire*, Comedia 1987.

19. See, e.g., Babsucio, op. cit., Jon Fortunato, *AIDS: The Spiritual Dilemma*, New York: Harper and Row 1987; Bill Kirkpatrick, *AIDS: Sharing the Pain*, Darton, Longman and Todd 1988. Many other books about counselling and pastoral care in general are, of course, relevant here. See, e.g., Michael Jacobs, *Still Small Voice*, SPCK 1982; Peter Speck and Ian Ainsworth-Smith, *Letting Go*, SPCK 1982.

20. Anthanasius, *On the Incarnation*, Mowbray 1953, p. 57.

21. Brandt, op. cit., p. 204.

Appendix B: Medico-Religious Dialogue and Co-operation: an Epilogue?

1. See e.g. Morton T. Kelsey, *Healing and Christianity*, SCM Press 1973, especially ch. 4.

2. See further e.g. Anthony Russell, *The Clerical Profession*, SPCK 1980, ch. 14; Michael MacDonald, *Mystical Bedlam*, Cambridge University Press 1981; Keith Thomas, *Religion and the Decline of Magic*, Penguin Books 1973; Darrell W. Amundsen and Gary B. Ferngren, 'Medicine and Religion: Early Christianity through the Middle Ages', and Roland L. Numbers and Ronald C. Sawyer, 'Medicine and Christianity in the Modern World' both in Martin E. Marty and Kenneth L. Vaux (eds), *Health/Medicine and the Faith Traditions*, Fortress Press 1982, and many papers in W. J. Shiels (ed.), *The Church and Healing*, Blackwell 1982.

3. See references in note 2 above, especially Amundsen and Ferngren, and Thomas, pp. 308f. See also Henry D. Rack, 'Doctors, Demons and Early Methods of Healing', in Shiels (ed.), op. cit.

4. See further Richard Palmer, 'The Church, Leprosy and Plague in Medieval and Modern Europe' in Shiels (ed.), op. cit., p. 138. For the plethora of non-medical and non-religious healers see Thomas, op. cit.

5. See Noel Parry and Jose Parry, *The Rise of the Medical Profession*, Croom Helm 1976.

6. See Russell, op. cit. on this phenomenon.

7. Heije Faber, *Pastoral Care in the Modern Hospital*, SCM Press 1971, p. 71.

8. Michael Wilson, Secretary of the Guild of Health in the early 1960s, kept a diary/scrapbook of his engagements and this documents in a fascinating way the rise of clergy-doctor associations which were often hailed with a blaze of local media publicity.

9. See *Contact* 11, 1964, p. 6. This number also contains an article by a GP, E. V. Kuensberg, 'Why we must get together' which in many ways encapsulates the spirit of the age to which I am referring.

10. See e.g. R. A. Lambourne, *Community, Church and Healing*, Darton, Longman & Todd 1963; Michael Wilson, *The Church is Healing*, SCM Press 1966; M. A. Melinsky, *Healing Miracles*, Mowbray 1968; Michael Wilson (ed.), *Explorations in Health and Salvation: A Selection of Papers by Bob*

Lambourne, Birmingham Institute for the Study of Worship and Religious Architecture 1983. See also numerous articles in early editions of *Contact*, itself a product of the 1960s. Early numbers of this journal included titles like 'What is Illness?' and Doctors and Clergy Meet' (see *Contact* 8 and 9, 1963, *Contact* 11, 1964). The *Religion and Medicine* volumes published by SCM Press for the Institute of Religion and Medicine 1970–76 also contain much material related to medico-theological dialogue and co-operation.

11. See Lambourne, op. cit. and Michael Wilson, *Health is for People*, Darton, Longman and Todd 1975, for the respective significance of community psychiatry and therapeutic communities. Murray Leishman and Bruce Ritson, 'Working Together at Fifty', *Contact* 50, 1975, gives an account of practical medico-theological co-operation in psychiatry with a community bias.

12. Institute of Religion and Medicine, *Newsletter* 61, 1983.

13. The Institute of Religion and Medicine recently published a fourth volume in the *Religion and Medicine* series: David Goodacre (ed.), *World Religions and Medicine*, Oxford: ILRM 1983. While this may be seen as a contra-indicator to the general case advanced here, it should be noted that this excellent volume is privately published, comes a long time after the other volumes in the series and is slighter (only 76pp). By dint of its title it devotes little space to dialogue and co-operation between Christian clerics and doctors.

14. R. A. Lambourne, 'Toward an Understanding of Medico-Theological Dialogue' in Wilson (ed.), op. cit.

15. Norman Autton, *Pastoral Care in Hospitals*, SPCK 1968, and *Pastoral Care of the Mentally Ill*, SPCK 1969.

16. See Stephen Pattison, 'Images of Inadequacy: Some Theoretical of Hospital Chaplaincy', *Contact* 69, 1980, pp. 6–15, for a critique of this traditional approach.

17. At its peak, the Institute of Religion and Medicine, for example, only had around 1200 members. See Institute of Religion and Medicine, *Newsletter* 61, 1983.

18. See David H. Clark, *Social Therapy in Psychiatry*, second ed. Churchill Livingstone 1981, preface.

19. In England and Wales whole-time medical practitioners in the NHS hospital service increased from 16,484 in 1961 to 22,059 in 1970 to 32,644 in 1982 (this final figure also includes dentists working in hospital service so is not directly comparable with the other two). Sources: DHSS, *Annual Report 1970*, HMSO 1970, Table 58; Medical Manpower Division, 'Medical and Dental Staffing Prospects in the NHS in England and Wales 1982', *Health Trends* 15, 1983, pp. 35–9.

20. In the last two decades two new specialist Royal Colleges have been set up for medical practitioners, the Royal Colleges of General Practitioners, and of Psychiatrists.

21. For an exposition of the medical model, see e.g. Wilson, *Health is for People*, ch. 1.

22. See further e.g. Lesley Doyal, *The Political Economy of Health*, Pluto 1979, ch. 5.

23. See e.g. Thomas McKeown, *The Role of Medicine*, Blackwell 1979, ch. 1; James McCormick, *The Doctor, Father Figure or Plumber?*, Croom Helm 1979.

24. See further Bryan Wilson, *Religion in Sociological Perspective*, Oxford University Press 1982, ch. 2.

25. For the marginalization of the clerical profession see Russell, op. cit., ch. 18.

26. Goodacre (ed.), op. cit., bears witness to the increasing significance of non-Christian faiths in British society.

27. For decline in the number of Anglican clergy in England see e.g. *The Church of England Yearbook 1974*, CIO 1974, Table XI, p. 166 which shews a sharp decline in ordinations throughout the 1960s from 636 pa in 1963 to 366 pa in 1972. Although it seems likely that the number of ordinations may be increasing again, many ordinands now are seeking non-stipendiary ministerial posts and are not employed full-time by the church. See *Statistical Supplement to the Church of England Yearbook 1981*, CIO 1981, Table 11.

28. Russell, op. cit. characterizes these as part of the charter role of ordained clergy as set out in the ordinal.

29. Bernice Martin, *A Sociology of Contemporary Cultural Change*, Blackwell 1981, pp. 190, 193.

30. See e.g. Morris Maddocks, *The Christian Healing Ministry*, SPCK 1981 and books reviewed in *Health and Healing* 4, 1983.

31. See e.g. Frank Wright, *Pastoral Care for Lay People*, SCM Press 1982; Ronald Metcalf, *Sharing Christian Ministry*, Mowbray 1981.

32. These developments were called for by Lambourne in *Community, Church and Healing*.

33. See Paul Wilding, *Professional Power and Social Welfare*, Routledge & Kegan Paul 1982, especially ch. 2; Alastair V. Campbell, *Moderated Love*, SPCK 1984.

34. See Ivan Illich, *Limits to Medicine*, Marion Boyars 1976; Ivan Illich et al., *Disabling Professions*, Marion Boyars 1977.

35. See e.g. McKeown, op. cit.; A. L. Cochrane, *Effectiveness and Efficiency*, np Nuffield Provincial Hospitals Trust 1971.

36. See e.g. Eliot Freidson, *Profession of Medicine*, Dodds, Mead 1975.

37. See e.g. David Tuckett, 'Doctors and Patients' in David Tuckett (ed.), *An Introduction to Medical Sociology*, Tavistock 1976.

38. See e.g. Irving Kenneth Zola, 'Medicine as an Institution of Social Control' in John Ehrenreich (ed.), *The Cultural Crisis of Modern Medicine*, Monthly Review Press, New York 1978; Peter Conrad and Joseph Schneider, *Deviance and Medicalization*, Mosby, St Louis 1980.

39. See Ian Kennedy, *The Unmasking of Medicine*, Allen and Unwin 1981, and Brian Inglis, *The Diseases of Civilization*, Granada 1981, p. xi.

40. See further e.g. Andrew Stanway, *Alternative Medicine*, Penguin Books

1979. There is great interest also in traditional and unqualified lay healers, see e.g. Mary Chamberlain, *Old Wives Tales*, Virago 1981. Current interest of this sort married to disillusion with professional and 'orthodox' qualifications perhaps provides a critique of the remark of the Rev. Martin Israel MB in the Institute of Religion and Medicine, *Newsletter* 60, 1983; 'The existence of the IRM is crucially important at our present time in history – a body of highly qualified people representing the spiritual and medical worlds of healing able to assess new trends in the healing ministry and to give positive guidance to the perplexed in its evaluation.'

41. This Appendix is a reproduction of my article of the same title, published in *Contact 84*, 1984, 8–17. It is reproduced here by kind permission of the Editor of *Contact*.

Index

AIDS, 13, 37, 91, 92, 310f.
Annointing, 47
Armstrong, David, 36
Asylums, 109ff.
Athanasius, 140
Autton, N., 151

Bell, Rudolph, 86
Bible, 12, 16
Black Report, 27, 73, 93
Body, The, 12, 20, 36, 64
Bonhoeffer, D., 101
Book of Common Prayer, 46, 52, 65
Brandt, Alan, 91, 130
British Medical Association, 94

Campbell, A., 150
Capitalism, 58
Charismatic movement, 51, 52ff.,
    58
Churches' Council for Health and
    Healing, 90
Class, 27, 53, 120, 123f.
Clergy, 153f.
Conflict (and healing), 98
Control (and illness), 85, 87, 97,
    101, 113, 122

Deliverance, ministry of, 16
Deviance, 29, 119
Devil, The, 107
Dialogue, 148f.
Diploma in Pastoral Studies, 149f.
Doctors, 60, 152f.
Depression, 99ff.
DHSS, 27
Dualism, 23

Elderly, 125
Erasmus, 106
Esclarin, A. P., 143
Electro-convulsive therapy (ECT),
    126
Eugel, G. L., 22, 23
Evil, 16, 102
Exorcism, 15, 129
Explanations, nature of, 11, 41ff.

Faber, H., 149
Faith, 102
Fear, 140f.
Foucault, Michel, 35
Fox, George, 84
Francis of Assisi, 76
Freidson, E., 97
Freud, S., 101, 115

God, 12, 49, 66ff., 102, 123
Guilt, 115
Guild of Health, 51

Habgood, J., 150
Hamel Cooke, E. C., 51
Health care professionals, 30, 31,
    82, 96, 148f.
Health education, 132
Heart disease, 25
Helman, Cecil, 33
Henson, Hensley, 52, 92
Hickson, J. M., 52
Hollenweger, W., 59
Homosexuality, 120, 131f., 139
Hospice, 88

Institutionalization, 117

191